Malcolm Jordan

Creative Design and Technology

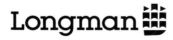

Longman

Contents

Part Three   Design problem examples

Introduction

What is design and technology? How does it differ from 'woodwork' and 'metalwork'?

The simple answer is that design and technology help solve three-dimensional problems in whatever is the most appropriate material, using all the different technical knowledge and skill that is available.

Design forms the core of the subject, by acting as the process in which we think out the solution to the problem. This starts by defining the problem and its limits – the **design brief**. This leads on to finding out all the background information about the problem, and factors that affect it. This is termed *research*. The research could involve finding out details from people, places, books, magazines, visit to a library, company or museum.

Using all this collected information, the problems can be thought out or *analysed*. This in turn starts to develop into simple **first ideas** for solving the problem, with a number of possible solutions. Each idea will have advantages and disadvantages; it may be that you choose to combine ideas. As further development of an idea takes place, technology is drawn upon to help solve areas of technical detail, such as which materials, construction processes etc., are to be used. The design and the technology go hand in hand, until you arrive at a final solution.

The final solution may well use a number of different materials, involving a wide range of production techniques and skills. These need to be understood and *planning* must take place before the practical stage, to avoid mistakes and to minimise problems. The final solution is now presented in an acceptable drawing form that can be understood for both production and possible sale. Once the design and planning are complete and the problem has a solution, it can now be *realised* or made.

This now involves the practical skills to make the idea become a reality. It may be that problems occur, or that details do not work as planned and certain points need to be re-designed. This is all part of the design core and is called *modification*.

After the solution or **prototype** has been made, it is normally tried and tested in use. This enables the practical solution to be judged as a success or not. This is termed the *evaluation*. It plays a vital part in design and technology, especially if the work and the designer are to improve and develop. It has to be remembered that the final idea or solution is only one answer to the problem, and many other solutions may be possible.

This book sets out to introduce the reader to design, its language, sources, methods of presentation. Alongside this is a vast range of related technology, such as materials, tools and processes. This information has been divided into sections for ease of understanding: **design, technology** and **project examples**. It should be remembered that this decision is artificial; in fact, all three are inter-related in practice. The technology section has been restricted to three main materials: **wood, plastics** and **metals**. Each is covered in some detail, as an understanding is needed in all three. However it should not be assumed that everything has been included, as space does not allow this in one book. If detailed specialist information is needed on one main material it is advisable to use a more advanced text book.

Throughout the book you will meet the following symbol: It has been added to reinforce safety and possible dangers from tools, materials and processes.

Part One

Design

1.1 DRAWING EQUIPMENT – THE BASIC SET

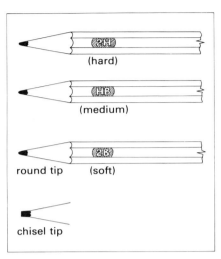

Fig. 1.1

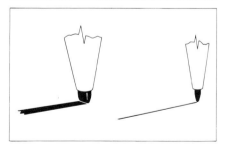

How do you think colour could spoil a design drawing?

Fig. 1.2

Colouring with paint tends to take a little longer than other methods. Why?

For any design work to be successful and easily understood, it must be presented in the best possible way. To do this, a good range of drawing equipment must be available to the designer so that work is not limited in any way. Start with a basic set of instruments such as a pencil, ruler, compass, rubber. This can extend to such things as drawing pens, stencils etc.

Some of the items needed for a good basic set of drawing equipment are listed.

Pencil

When starting design work the pencil is the most important item of equipment, being able to convey ideas very quickly by drawings and sketches on paper. The types of drawing will not, however, all be the same; some will need hard, accurate lines while others will need soft, easy flowing lines. Pencils are made in a range of different quality leads, from very very hard (9H) down to very very soft (6B). In general design work three different grades will cover most of the work: 2H for accurate working drawings; HB for general drawing and notes; 2B for good sketching and shading. Any pencil will only work well if it is kept sharp. It can have either a rounded tip or a chisel edge, depending on which the designer prefers.

Colour system

Coloured pencils or crayons – to help with the presentation of a drawing some form of colour can be used to emphasise a shape or an outline. A simple and ideal way of doing this is to use coloured pencils or crayons. The colours they give tend to be a little dull and have a grain effect but they can bring a plane pencil drawing to life. A spray varnish can be used to stop the colour from rubbing off.

Felt tip pens – provide another simple method of applying colour, in a water-based form that is quick drying. Two types are available: the large felt tip for colour-washing areas, and the finer nylon tip for line work. The colours are bright and clean but can fade over a period of time or if left out in bright sunlight.

Paint

For more advanced work the ideal colour system is paint; the advantage being that the colours can be mixed to any shade needed. The best type for design work is *Gouache*. This can be used with water but gives brilliant colours and dries quite quickly. Also, the colour does not tend to fade like the felt tip. They do, however, need a range of brushes from fine to broad tip so that they can be applied for different types of work.

Other basic equipment

Drawing board

This can be any simple, rectangular board, with straight sides and a flat surface. The overall size will depend on how large the drawings or paper will

Drawing pins can be used to hold the paper in position on a board. What damage can they cause?

be. The two normal size boards, shown in Fig. 1.3, are designed for two standard paper sizes: A2 and A3. These fit on to the boards with a little room to spare.

Drawing guides

Used with the drawing board is some form of drawing guide for drawing true horizontal lines. This can be either a *Tee square* which is loose and has to be held and guided by hand, or a special fixture called a *parallel motion*. The latter only needs to be moved up and down as it is held in a horizontal position. By using these aids, lines can be drawn quickly across the paper.

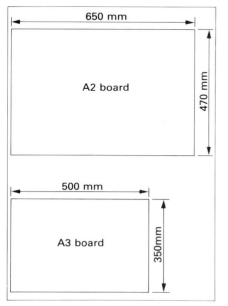

Fig. 1.3

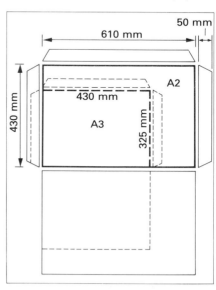

Fig. 1.4

Fig. 1.5

Other items

There is a wide range of useful items:
— a good rubber
— plastic set squares for drawing accurate angled or vertical lines
— an accurate compass
— spring clips for holding the paper
— a 300 mm steel ruler for measuring.
These will all prove to be very useful parts of a design kit. They are vital when the stage is reached for very accurate working drawings to be drawn up. Once a kit is built up the design work can be done almost anywhere. This allows great freedom.

These extra items can be added to the kit:
— a small modelling knife
— a glue stick
— a letter stencil
— curve aids.
These should be added as the standard of the work develops and expands.

One of the major needs for design drawing work is a folder that can hold design sheets. The outline shape of a folder is given in Fig. 1.5, plus the overall sizes for A2 and A3. Make up the folder from stiff card. Join the side pieces with tape. Add some cord or tape as a carrying handle.

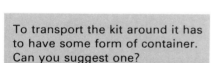

To transport the kit around it has to have some form of container. Can you suggest one?

1.2 LINE, SHAPE AND FORM

Before a designer can start to tackle a problem, he or she must have certain basic skills and methods of expressing ideas quickly and well. The first skill must be the ability to communicate in the form of a drawing. A good design drawing can convey ideas and information far quicker than a whole page of words.

The line

This will form the starting point for most design drawing work. The way a line is put down will play an important part in how the final drawing is understood.

Let us start by first drawing a line on a sheet of paper with an HB pencil, without the use of any aids. This is called *freehand*. The line we draw is not accurate but it does convey a feeling of direction. The direction will depend on whether the line is drawn vertical or horizontal, sloping or curved.

What type of line will the HB pencil tend to give, hard or soft?

Fig. 1.6

The quality of the line will depend on how hard we press on the pencil and the speed at which we draw the line. These two points play an important part in freehand drawing; for example, when starting to work out a design idea the lines need to be quite feint so that they do not need to be rubbed out. Yet when completing a drawing the line should be firm and hard so that it can be seen and understood. If we draw the line slowly it tends to be thick and wavy; if drawn quickly it tends to be feint and much straighter.

Draw lines on paper at different speeds and of different thickness.

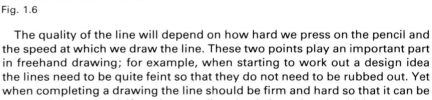

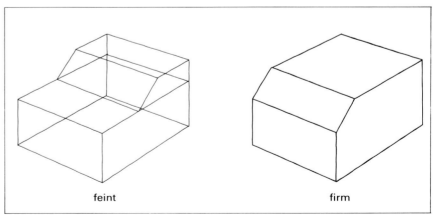

feint   firm

Fig. 1.7

Fig. 1.8 'Sharpness and aggression'

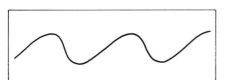

Fig. 1.9 'Gentleness and rhythm'

The line can also be used to create other meanings such as movement, texture, rhythm, and even shapes and form. For example, if we draw a line as

shown in Fig. 1.8 we can create the feeling of sharpness and aggression.
If we change it slightly we can create a feeling of gentleness and rhythm.

Copy the lines drawn in Fig 1.10. Add your own titles of what you think they could represent.

Fig. 1.10

By changing the length, direction and closeness of lines, we can create an impression of light and shade and even texture.

Line patterns

When lines change direction and start to repeat in a regular way, *patterns* begin to develop. These can be used to great effect by the designer to create interest and rhythm in an object that is perhaps dull and boring. For example,

Create patterns of your own, first using continuous lines, then using a series of short lines that repeat.

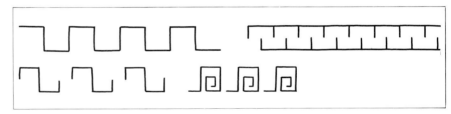

Fig. 1.11   Line patterns

a simple line pattern could add to the appearance of a plain silver beaker — as shown in Fig. 1.12.

Line shapes

As lines start to cross over each other and enclose a space they begin to create *shapes*. This can be done with straight or curved lines. It could be developed, as shown in Fig. 1.14, to create free design shapes that could be used for decoration or appearance.

Fig. 1.12   Silver beaker

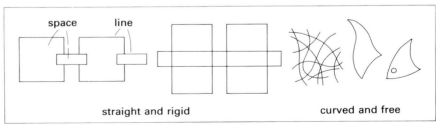

Fig. 1.14   Silver beaker

It is important to remember that it is not only the lines that form the shape but the space both inside and outside the lines. The shape or **plane**, as it is sometimes called, is a flat two-dimensional surface. It is the first major method for representing objects on paper. Each shape or plane has an overall width and length.

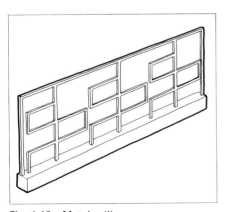

Fig. 1.13   Metal railings

Line, shape and form

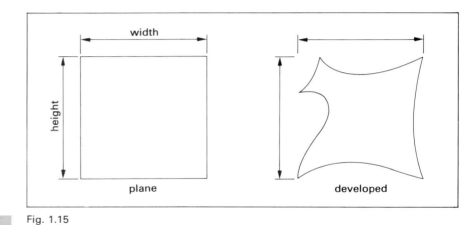

Fig. 1.15

These shapes or planes can be developed within themselves, or be overlapped by others, or even be penetrated by others to create many different effects. They can represent a solid object such as a wooden door or be transparent like sheet glass. They can be as open as a ring, or as twisted as a spring.

Shapes can also be formed by using a series of different length lines to cover an area. Try this out in the way shown in Fig. 1.17.

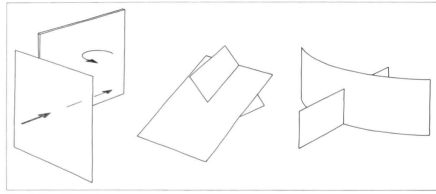

Fig. 1.16   Plane shapes

Fig. 1.17   Line shapes

As we have seen, when lines cross at random the shape is uncontrolled; but if they are drawn in a regular manner, it is possible to form geometrical and natural shapes.

Geometrical shapes

These shapes are a major source for design ideas, providing an ideal starting point for the designer when working on a project. The line can be used to

How many sides do the following polygons have:
a) pentagon
b) octagon
c) heptagon?

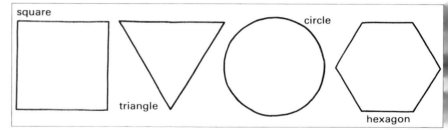

Fig. 1.18

draw up the many different geometrical shapes known. These range from the square, triangle, circle and hexagon to the highly complicated many-sided polygons. These shapes are not limited to two-dimensional drawing but can be used when the drawing becomes three dimensional or has depth, as we will see later.

To develop geometrical shapes for further design use, we can develop them in a number of ways:

1. A simple figure such as a triangle can be divided into two pieces by using a straight line. This starts to create interesting spaces and shapes. If we vary the size of the pieces, more interest is created, but balance is retained. This can be developed by using two lines, and so on.

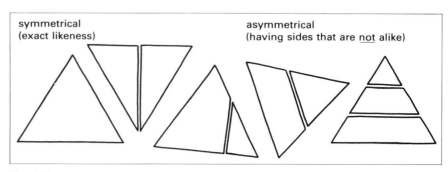

Fig. 1.19

2. If instead of the straight line we use a curved line, we develop a whole new range of shapes (Fig. 1.20).

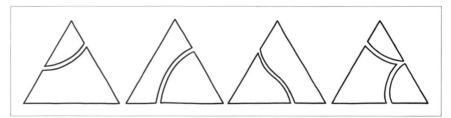

Fig. 1.20

> Try this out with another geometrical shape and develop it in your own way.

3. If the drawing is done on card, a further stage in the development of the shape can be provided. This is done by cutting up the card according to the lines, straight or curved. Then move the pieces apart to create different spaces and shapes (Fig. 1.21).

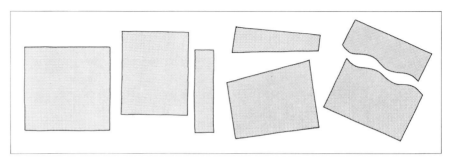

Fig. 1.21

Further cutting and movement of the pieces, such as reversing or overlapping, can lead to the development of interesting shapes and patterns.

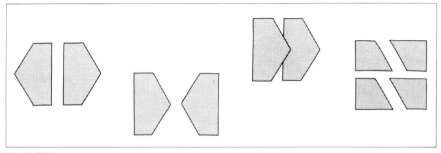

Fig. 1.22

The use of colour, tone and texture can be added to the parts or pieces to give many different effects.

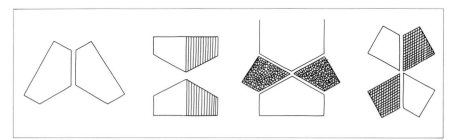

Fig. 1.23

A further development is the introduction of a second geometrical shape, which can be added to the original shape or cut from it (Fig. 1.24).

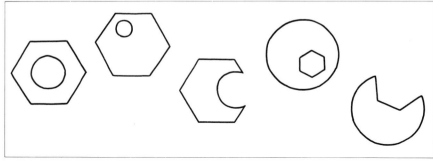

Fig. 1.24

Here are some examples of practical items that have evolved from geometrical shapes.

These then are just some of the suggested avenues that a designer needs to explore in search of interesting shapes. They will form the starting point for many of the design problems we will meet in design and technology.

Natural shapes

Another design source is Nature itself, providing endless material for the designer. Such things as leaves, fruit and nuts can all act as the starting point for a piece of design work. More advanced work can use such things as fish, birds or insects. These are a little more difficult to develop without experience.

Sometimes the object or part of the object is looked at under a microscope. Can you think why?

Fig. 1.25

To use natural shapes as a design base, we should start with a simple object such as a leaf. This needs to be researched and drawn. Be careful to look at the different forms it could take, the colour, pattern and texture. All these may be used as a starting point.

Research shapes

These can be drawn up using simple line drawings (Fig. 1.26).

Research another natural form such as fruit or grasses. Draw up several different types. In the case of fruit, cut it in half and copy the internal structure.

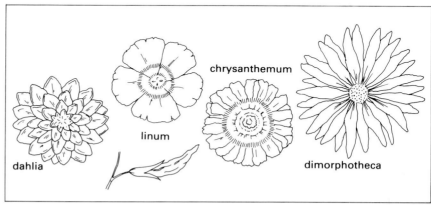

dahlia

linum

chrysanthemum

dimorphotheca

Fig. 1.26

Once a number of line drawings are made the design process can start. The designer cannot hope to improve the flower form. What he or she tries to do is to simplify and so extract shapes.

If we use the Linum as an interesting flower, the form could be simplified as shown in Fig. 1.27.

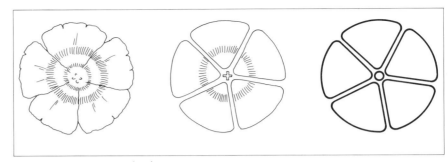

Fig. 1.27   A good simple shape

The simple shape can also be developed by:

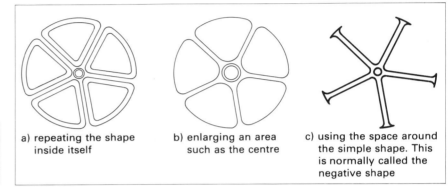

a) repeating the shape inside itself

b) enlarging an area such as the centre

c) using the space around the simple shape. This is normally called the negative shape

Fig. 1.28

Draw these shapes and then experiment with different colours and textures to highlight them.

Instead of using the whole shape a small part of the object can bring forward new ideas of interest. In Fig. 1.29 a petal has been developed.

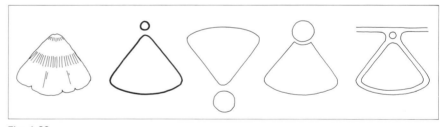

Fig. 1.29

The stamen in the centre of the flower may also prove to be an interesting area for developing. Again start by simplifying the natural shapes.

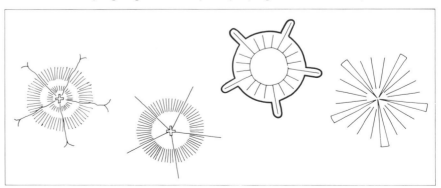

Develop the natural form you researched earlier in a similar way.

Fig. 1.30

1   Design

These then are just some of the ways in which the designer will build up his or her design shapes. Keep all of your drawings in a design source folder. They could lead to such things as jewellery design, furniture design, decoration for materials, ceramics, architecture and many other designs. As an example, the flower design shapes that were developed above, could be used to help with the following items (Fig. 1.31).

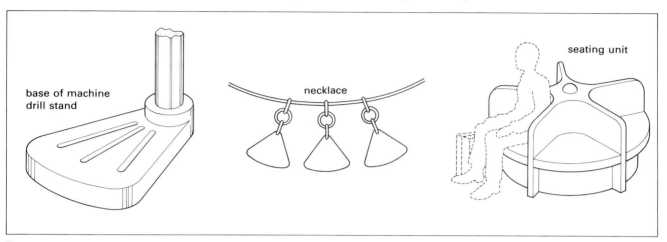

Fig. 1.31

The line can also help us to move one stage on and create the illusion of giving the two-dimensional shape another dimension or *form*. When this happens the drawing is said to be three dimensional, and is made up of a number of shapes or planes. This happens by adding further lines to a single shape. These lines may be straight, angled or curved. When joined up they are able to give the impression of real objects or forms.

Again, like shapes, geometrical forms play an important part in the development of design work. Such things as the cube, cylinder, pyramid, prism or sphere can all be used as the building blocks upon which to develop an idea or design.

Why should the sphere be a difficult form to create on a flat sheet of paper?

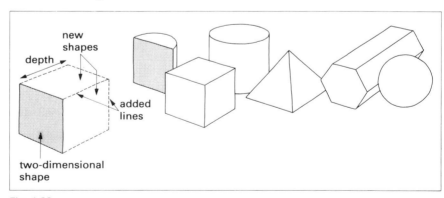

Fig. 1.32

Form, like shape, can be developed by adding different forms together, cutting up the form, overlapping, repeating etc.

Three-dimensional drawing is the most realistic way we have of drawing objects on paper. It can show most of the main features in a single sketch.

Develop some geometrical forms by building them together in one unit as shown in Fig. 1.33.

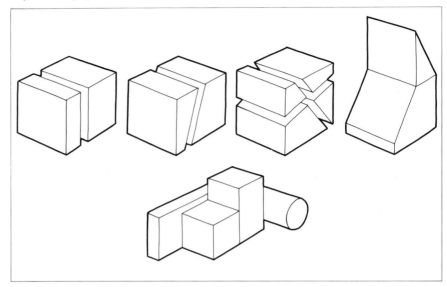

Fig. 1.33

If the drawing is to look real or correct, two important points must be considered as we draw: a) size, b) proportion.

Size

If the final drawing is to be understood, the size of the object in relation to other things around or close by must be made clear. In this way an object such as a ring, which could be large or small, can only be judged in relation to the finger on which it should fit. So whenever we draw an object, we should try to add other features so that comparisons can be made for size.

Proportions

This means that the drawing of an object should have the correct natural balance between parts of itself or with things that are related. This may be sizes, complexity, texture, colour etc. For example, if we look at the drawings shown in Fig. 1.35 we can see that the handle is too small for the jug or it is out of proportion.

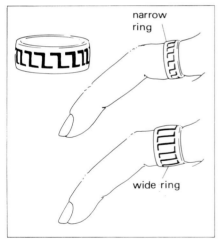

Fig. 1.34

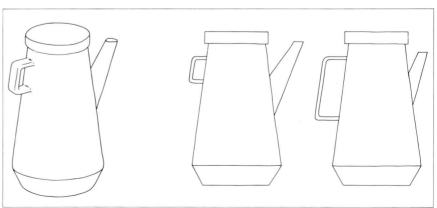

Fig. 1.35

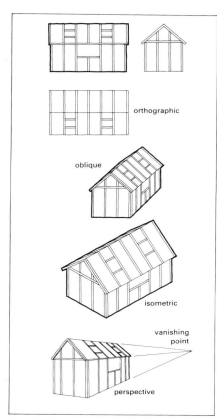

Fig. 1.36

Draw what you think the toy train would look like from above (3).

We have seen how it is possible to have two distinct types of drawing; those that are *two* dimensional and those that are *three* dimensional. Both systems are used by the designer a great deal – from simple ideas to complex working drawings. The way in which they are drawn, however, does vary a great deal. It varies according to how much information the drawing has to convey, how true the drawing needs to be. Four main methods are used in general and they may be presented in freehand form or by using instruments.

1. *Orthographic projection* – a two-dimensional way of drawing. It is used for working or detail types of drawing such as in engineering, building, furniture.

2. *Oblique drawing* – a three-dimensional way of drawing that is very simple to construct but does tend to be a little distorted. Ideal when the object has a curved front view.

3. *Isometric drawing* – another three-dimensional method of drawing, that is drawn up to the correct sizes. It gives a slightly distorted illustration. Suitable for small construction details, parts, etc.

4. *Perspective drawing* – the most realistic of all the three-dimensional methods of drawing. It is ideal as a final presentation system. The sizes, however, cannot be measured due to the natural vanishing points of an object.

We can cover the different methods of drawing by using our freehand line again. This is by far the quickest way of recording ideas. It should not be thought of as a poor and rough way of presenting work, so we should do it with care.

Orthographic projection

When we looked at two-dimensional shapes earlier we saw, in fact, a *view*. We can do the same thing with most objects. The shape we draw will depend on which way we view the object – from the front, from the side, from the top, etc. For example, if we look at a toy train from the front (1), the view could look like Fig. 1.38. If we look at it from the side (2), the view will have changed to Fig. 1.39.

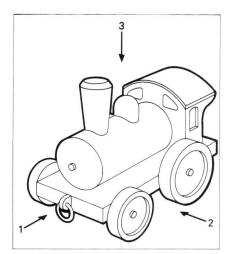

Fig. 1.37

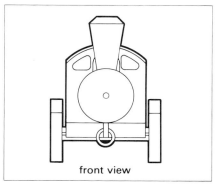

front view

Fig. 1.38

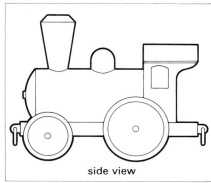

side view

Fig. 1.39

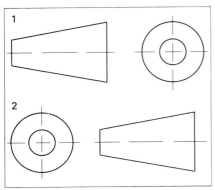

Fig. 1.40

As we have seen, each view contains different information. By drawing only one view a great deal would be missing for someone trying to understand the object. To overcome this we need to draw three different views to get a complete picture of the object. However, if they are drawn anywhere on the sheet, they could be mistaken for three different objects. So we need to put the three views in related positions to each other, to show they are all the same object. This form of drawing is called *orthographic projection*. It is very much a technical form of drawing.

There are two ways of doing orthographic projection:

1. *First angle projection*;
2. *Third angle projection*.

Both systems are used world wide; some countries favour one method, others favour the other. The relevant small symbol is always added to the drawing to explain which has been used.

First angle projection

Imagine the perfume package shown in Fig. 1.41 suspended in the corner of a box. The view we see from the front would be drawn on the box surface behind. This is the **front view or elevation**. If we now look from the side and draw the view we see on the surface behind, we obtain the **side elevation**. Then we repeat the method looking from the top. This gives us the **plan**.

Why use a symbol on the drawing and not words?

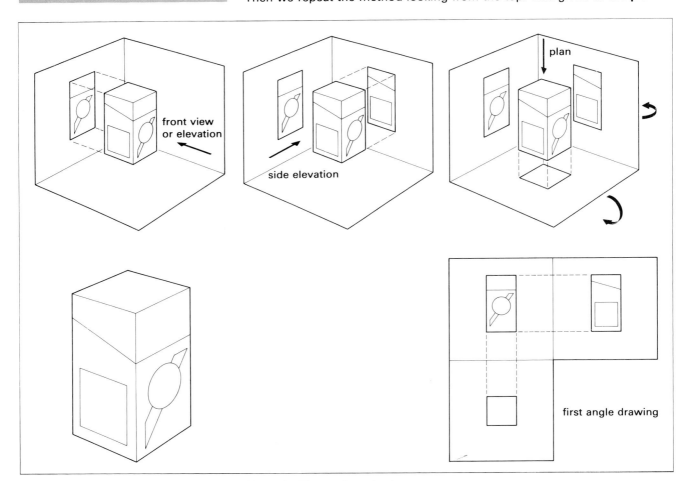

Fig. 1.41 First angle projection

When we remove the object we are left with three different views on the sides of the box. If we now open out the box, we will have our first angle drawing. The views are all in related positions to each other.

This then is how the views will look, but of course we have to draw them on a flat sheet of paper not in a box. We have to use a form of framework to help keep the three views in line.

We start by sketching out the front view of the object on a base line. From this we extend feint lines vertically and horizontally.

Find out what the word projection really means when used in drawing.

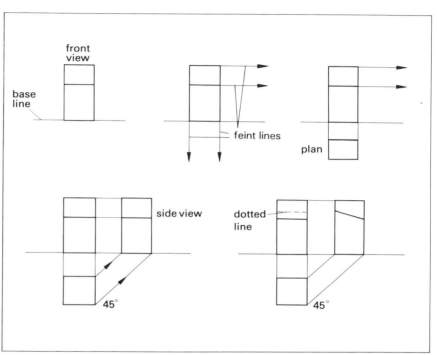

Fig. 1.42

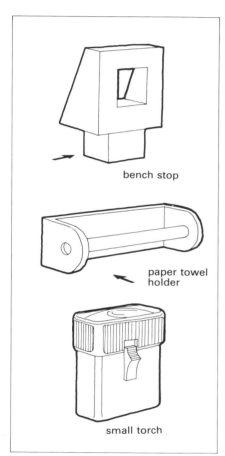

bench stop

paper towel holder

small torch

Fig. 1.43

Sketch out what you think the objects in Fig. 1.43 would look like in first angle projection.

Using the vertical lines as a guide, we can now add the plan view underneath the front view. To complete the side view we need to sketch feint lines from the plan at 45° until they reach the base line. The 45° lines change at the base line into vertical lines. As the two sets of lines cross they form the side view. Now all three views are in related positions.

Once all three views are in place the outline of each can be drawn over with a firm line.

Sometimes the three views have details that cannot be seen from the views shown. To show that they are hidden from view, we use a dotted line or hidden detail line. For example, the perfume box has a hinged line. We show this by means of a dotted line.

Third angle projection

To view the object this time we cover it with an imaginary glass box. On the surface we copy the view that is seen inside. This time we have the front view before the object, the side view on the outside, and the plan appears on the top of the glass box.

If we open out the box as before, we can see that the side view comes to the left of the front view, and the plan is in a related position above. This is *third angle projection*.

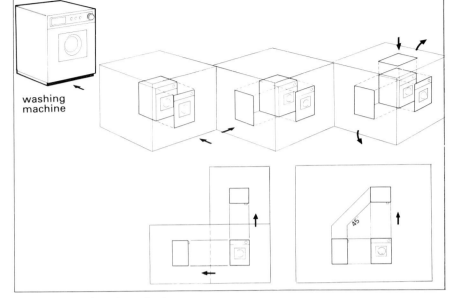

washing machine

Fig. 1.44   Third angle projection

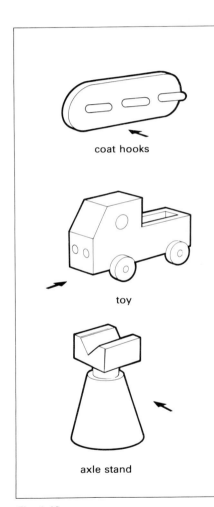

coat hooks

toy

axle stand

Fig. 1.46

Sketch out the objects in Fig. 1.46 using third angle projection.

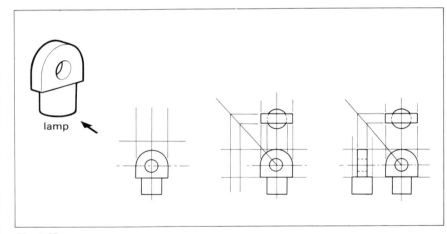

lamp

Fig. 1.45

The method of sketching on paper is similar to first angle projection, but the feint lines need to be to the left and above, as shown in Fig. 1.44.

A further example is given in Fig. 1.45 using a curved object.

Sectioning

The dotted line is limited when explaining hidden details. It cannot fully show what is happening inside an object. To overcome this problem and to show the inside detail, the object is imagined to be cut in half. Any of the three views can be tackled in this way, and is again drawn in the related position. Any view drawn in this way is called a *sectional* view.

The point at which the object is cut is marked by a special *sectional line* on one of the other normal views. Arrowheads are added to the line to help explain which way the cut object is being viewed.

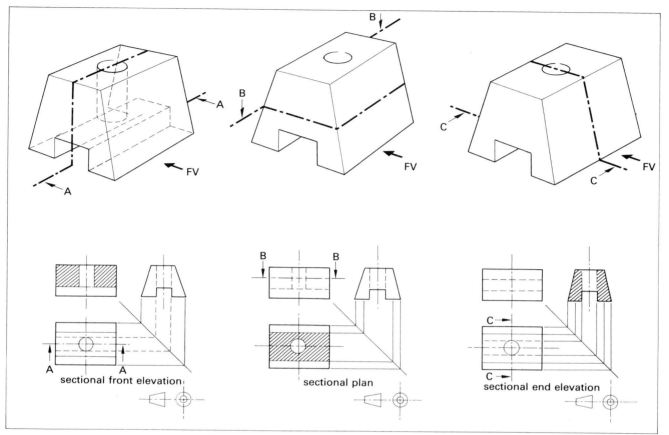

Fig. 1.47   Sectioning

Sketch out what you would think the correct sectional view would look like for the objects in Fig. 1.48.

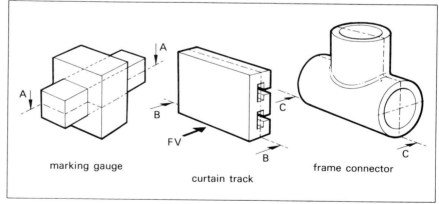

Fig. 1.48

This then is orthographic projection in a simple freehand form. It will lead on to the final accurate working or presentation drawings with instruments. Nonetheless, it plays a very valuable part in this form; things can be planned out quickly, altered or changed if necessary, and mistakes can be corrected before the careful, accurate final drawings are started.

Oblique drawing

This form of drawing starts with a two-dimensional view. For example, take the front view and add feint angled lines. The lines are normally drawn at 45 degrees. They all travel in the same direction, keeping parallel to each other. The third dimension is now marked on the angled lines, and the points are joined up to give a three-dimensional figure (Fig. 1.49).

The object does, however, look somewhat distorted. This can be improved by making the *depth half size*. (See Fig. 1.50.)

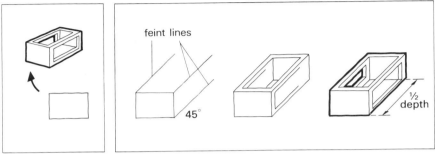

Fig. 1.49   Fig. 1.50

It is an ideal system for drawing an object with a curved view at the front, as this can be drawn with a compass. Any further curves that are on the same centre line can also be drawn with a compass.

If the curve is on the angled lines it has to be drawn freehand, after first plotting out the approximate position.

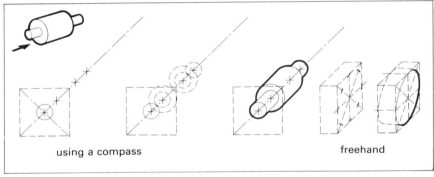

Fig. 1.51

Convert the first angle projection drawing in Fig. 1.52 into an oblique drawing

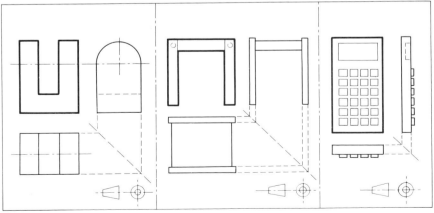

Fig. 1.52

Sometimes the object has no true shape to work from at the front. When this happens the figure must be drawn as if it is in an imaginary box or crate. The box is drawn to the overall sizes of the object. Then the detail is worked inside the shape.

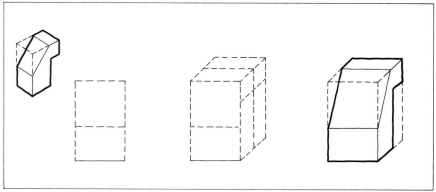

Fig. 1.53

Although the oblique drawing tends to look distorted, it does have the advantage of being able to convey correct sizes of lines.

Isometric drawing

This is a much less distorted way of drawing an object in three dimensions, using the correct sizes. With this system we look at one corner of the object, and draw this as a vertical line. From this corner 30°-angled lines are drawn to the right and left. These lines represent the horizontal sides of the object. The true sizes are measured on these lines. The shape is built up with more vertical and more 30°-angled lines.

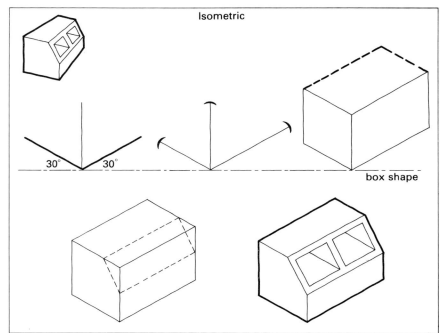

Fig. 1.54   Isometric

In Fig. 1.54 you can see how the vertical line starts at the corner, and how the 30° lines are drawn to build up the overall box shape from the height, width and length. Once the outline is planned, the inside detail can be started and built up from the vertical and angled lines.

The curved surface is a little more difficult in isometric drawing. All the faces of the drawing are not true so a compass cannot be used. To help with this, guide lines are normally used to reduce the amount of guesswork as to the correct shape. An example is shown in Fig. 1.55.

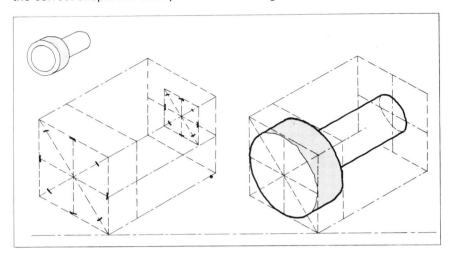

Fig. 1.55

Convert the drawings in Fig. 1.56 into isometric drawings.

For more accurate curved work, a true view is drawn, then divided up with grid lines. These grid lines are now transferred to the isometric drawing and the curved points are plotted. The final curve line is added to complete the shape.

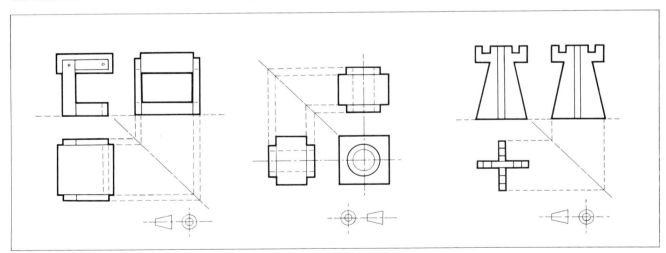

Fig. 1.56

1 Design

Exploded isometric

Isometric drawing can be very useful when a drawing is needed to explain how an object is made up, showing how the different parts fit together and in what position. This is done by imagining the object pulled apart or exploded, yet keeping all the pieces in related positions (Fig. 1.57).

How do you think exploded isometric drawings are used in car repair manuals.

Draw the objects in Fig. 1.59 in exploded isometric.

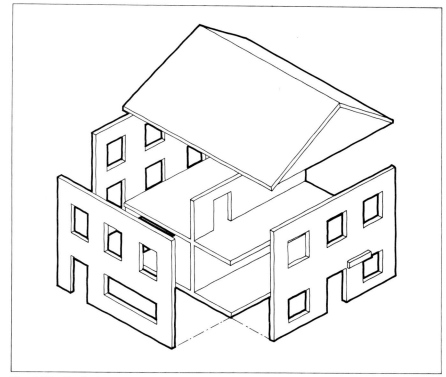

Fig. 1.57 Exploded isometric

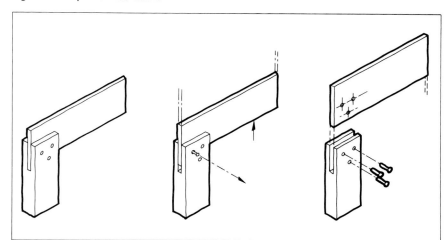

Fig. 1.58

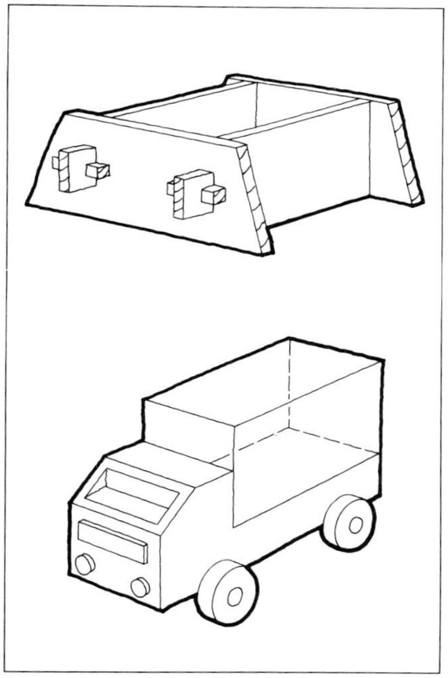

It is done by drawing the feint isometric view of the object, then extending the vertical and angled lines. The pieces are now built up again a short distance from each other, giving the impression of an unassembled object.

This method is used a great deal for such things as do-it-yourself instructions, repair manuals, etc.

Fig. 1.59

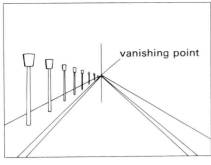

Fig. 1.60

Perspective drawing

When we need to view an object in the most realistic way possible, we have to use perspective drawing. This is because in real life objects seem to reduce in size the further away they are. For example, if we look straight down a road, we know it is parallel yet it appears to finish on the horizon as a single point. This is called the **vanishing point**. (See Fig. 1.60.) Lamp-posts at the side of the road seem to get smaller in size, but we know they are all the same size. To copy this natural view of objects we can use two methods of perspective drawing:

1. single point perspective;
2. two point perspective.

Single point perspective

This can be used in two ways for drawing: first to present single objects; and second to present a total scene such as a room.

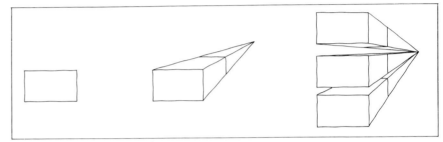

Fig. 1.61

To draw a single object, we first have to draw a straight view – the front, for instance. We can now place the vanishing point above, to one side or below, depending on what our horizon needs to be. Feint lines are now used to join up the view and single point. These act as guide lines. The depth of the object has to be marked on the feint lines. As the object is getting smaller these lines have to be judged and not measured. From the examples given in Fig. 1.61 you can see how the viewpoint changes.

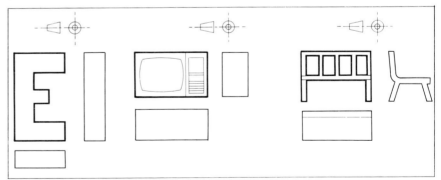

Fig. 1.62

Try out the one point perspective on the drawings in Fig. 1.62.

The single point perspective is perhaps best used for large scenes, when the vanishing point appears within the drawing. This can add a feeling of depth to the view, and can be used for room design work, stage design work, garden designs, buildings and architecture.

To use this method, we start with a rectangle of the total scene. For example, if this was a room it would be a rectangle based on the width and height of the room. Inside the rectangle place the horizon line with the vanishing point. This will vary according to how we view the scene; for example, sitting in a chair, standing up, or standing on steps. Once the point is fixed, all depth lines are joined to this. Horizontal and vertical lines are used to form the shapes.

Fig. 1.63

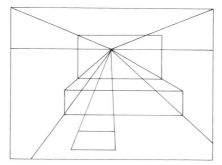
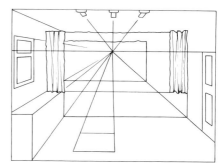

Copy the view shown in Fig. 1.63. Then try this method out on drawing of a room at home.

Two point perspective

This system of drawing gives the most realistic view possible when used for a single object. This could be anything from a small table to a large house. With this method we view a corner of the object, and the two sides reduce along vanishing lines to two points on the horizon.

To draw this out we start with the horizontal line, and place two points some distance apart. The corner height of the object is then drawn midway between the points. It can be drawn in any position above, on or below the horizon, depending on the view required (1). Lines are now joined from the corner to the points (2). Depth marks are made along these lines (3). Each side is built up by using vertical lines for the heights. All other lines vanish to the points, as shown (4).

Draw the object in Fig. 1.65 in two point perspective.

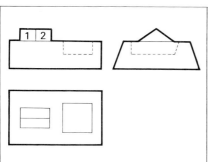

Fig. 1.65

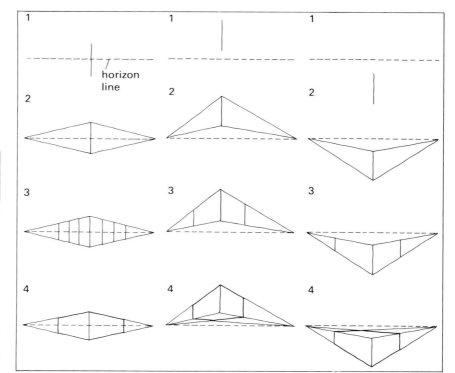

Fig. 1.64   Two point perspective

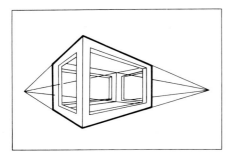

Fig. 1.66

It is possible to have one vanishing point nearer to the object than the other. This will depend on how it is viewed. An example is shown in Fig. 1.66.

When curves or circles have to be drawn, we again use the feint box method used in isometric drawing. This time, however, the box reduces in size the further it is away so the curves inside will also reduce.

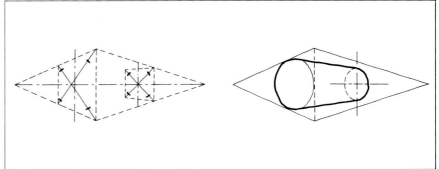

Fig. 1.67

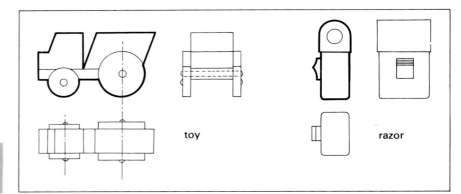

toy   razor

Fig. 1.68

Draw the curved shapes in Fig. 1.68 in two point perspective.

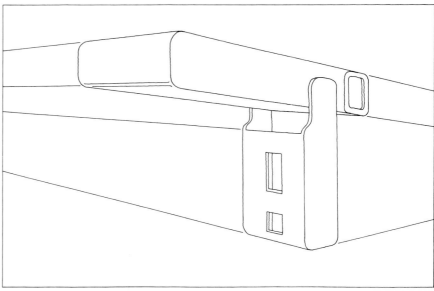

Fig. 1.69

Once the system is understood, it is possible not to use the points on the paper as the drawings would have to remain quite small. When drawing large views, imagine the two points somewhere off the paper and draw the guide lines to these. Alternately, use drawing pins at the vanishing points with cotton to indicate the lines. In this way, the view does not become distorted or have to remain small.

1.4 HIGHLIGHTING DRAWINGS

It is possible to add other graphic elements to the simple pencil drawing. These include shadow lines, shading, colour and texture techniques. This can help to highlight drawings or areas of drawings, making them stand out. They can bring a dull drawing to life.

Shadow lines

With this method the pencil drawing is given a thicker or shadow line. This can be either a total outline or along each edge that has a hidden side. Some examples are given in Fig. 1.70.

A curved object can be treated in the same way. Colour can be used in this way with either felt tip pens or crayons.

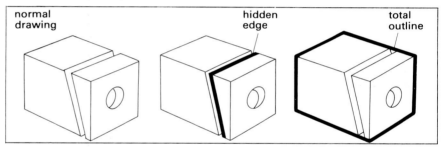

Fig. 1.70   Highlighting

Shading

When we view an object, much of what we see are not edges or lines of the object but the amount of light that is reflected from its surfaces. We can copy this by shading: the darkest part is the area furthest from the light. Some

Try this method out on one of your earlier three-dimensional drawings.

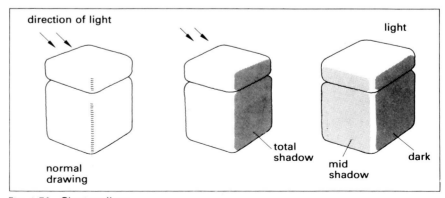

Fig. 1.71   Shadow lines

parts will be very bright while others will be quite dark. An example of how this is done is shown in Fig. 1.71.

Curved objects have a reducing amount of light on their curved surfaces. With these objects, we leave a strip of light and darken the surfaces gradually towards the outer edge.

Colour can be used in shading. It is best done with the designers' gouache paint to get the depth of tone.

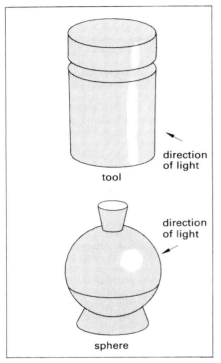

direction of light

tool

direction of light

sphere

Fig. 1.72

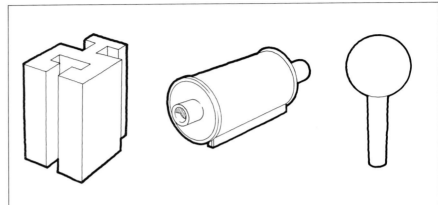

Fig. 1.73

Texture techniques

We can attempt to improve the drawing of an object by giving an impression of the material from which it is made. Designers represent the material texture, by using lines, circles or dots — or a combination of all these. Some simple examples are given in Fig. 1.74.

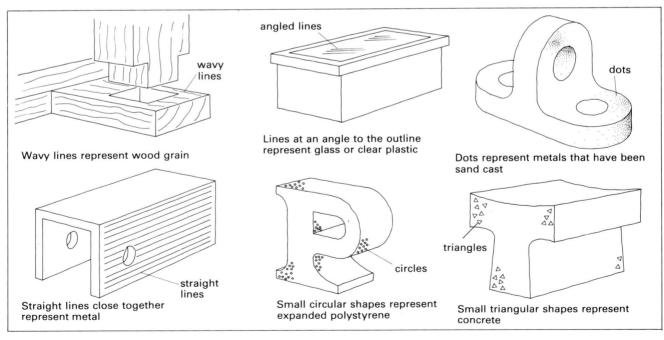

wavy lines

Wavy lines represent wood grain

angled lines

Lines at an angle to the outline represent glass or clear plastic

dots

Dots represent metals that have been sand cast

straight lines

Straight lines close together represent metal

circles

Small circular shapes represent expanded polystyrene

triangles

Small triangular shapes represent concrete

Fig. 1.74 Textures

1 Design

These are just some of the ways texture can be attempted. However, on many occasions the designer draws his or her own idea of a given texture.

Draw the items in Fig. 1.75.
Add the correct type of texture.

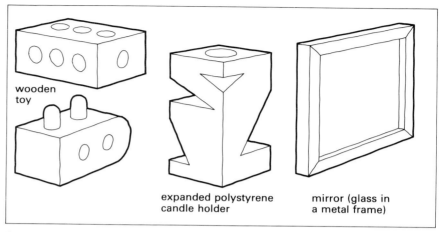

wooden toy

expanded polystyrene candle holder

mirror (glass in a metal frame)

Fig. 1.75

1.5 WORKING AND PRESENTATION DRAWINGS

We have looked at all the different methods of drawing – oblique, isometric, perspective and orthographic – but only in a freehand form. While this is ideal for starting and developing ideas, it tends to be limited. More accurate work needs sizes and proportions. To obtain this standard we need to use instruments such as the compass, set squares, ruler, drawing board and tee square, etc.

Working drawings

Why do working drawings need to be accurate?

Once an idea is finalised and the object designed, an accurate working drawing has to be drawn up. This will contain all the necessary information such as sizes, materials, number of parts, how it fits together, etc. The main system used is the orthographic projection; however, the pictorial methods are used to explain how the object is to be assembled.

Formal orthographic drawing

This form of drawing is covered by special regulations called British Standards 308, in which the style and method of drawing are kept to simple strict lines. In this way, a drawing can be understood by everyone, from the designer who has drawn it to the person who has to make up the object.

Types of lines

As we discussed earlier, in this type of drawing, lines are given strict meanings. Each line explains something about the object. See Fig. 1.76 for details.

	Types of lines	Description	Use
(a)	———————	A continuous thick line	Outlines
(b)	———————	A continuous thin line	Projection lines
(c)	– – – – – –	Short dashes	Hidden detail
(d)	–·—·—·—	A long chain	Centre lines
(e)	↑·—·—·↑	A long chain with arrows	A cutting or section line
(f)	◄——————►	A thin line with arrows	A dimensioning line
(g)	/////////	Thin 45°=angled lines	To show a surface has been cut. They are called hatching lines

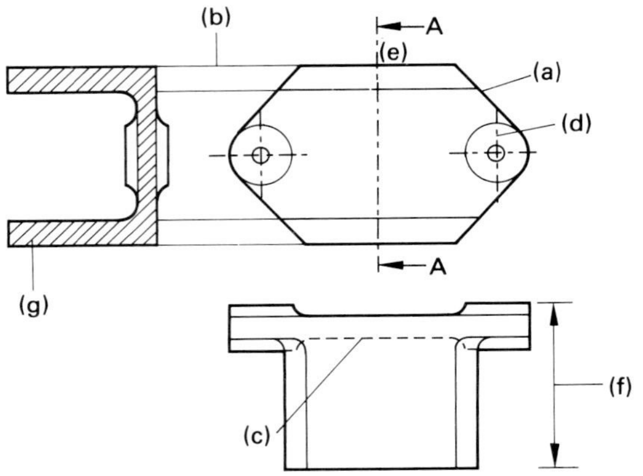

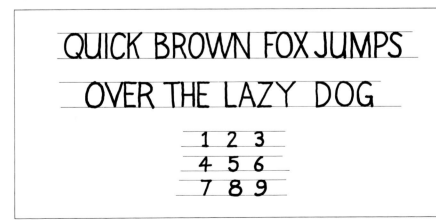

Fig. 1.76

Lettering

This is also covered by the British Standards. It is in the simple form shown in Fig. 1.77.

Copy out the lettering and numbers in Fig. 1.77. Use guide lines to help.

QUICK BROWN FOX JUMPS
OVER THE LAZY DOG

1 2 3
4 5 6
7 8 9

Fig. 1.77

1 Design

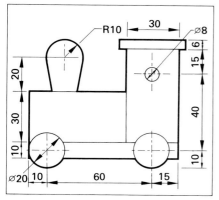

Fig. 1.78

Why do you think a symbol (∅) is used for the diameter sign?

What would the scale be for a line 30mm long that is drawn as 10mm?

What is the correct length of a line 20mm long if it has been drawn to a scale of 1:10?

Dimensions

The way the drawing is dimensioned or has the measurements added is also covered by British Standards. This is so that they can be read or understood quickly without interfering with the outline of the drawing. The general rule is that they should be clear of the drawing and well spaced; all vertical dimensions should be read from the bottom to the top of the sheet. An example is shown in Fig. 1.78.

Scale

If the work to be drawn is very small or large, it will have to be adapted to fit the sheet of paper; a suitable scale has to be used. For example, if the object is 1000mm long, you may decide to draw the length as 500mm on the paper so that it will fit: this is a line drawn to a scale of 2:1. Similarly a line 10 mm long, drawn to a scale of 1:5, would represent 50mm. All other lines have to be scaled down in the same way. However, all the dimensions that are written on the drawing will indicate the correct size, with the scale ratio noted in the title block (see page 31).

Conventions

The Standards also try to simplify difficult details that have to be drawn. Some examples are given in Fig. 1.79.

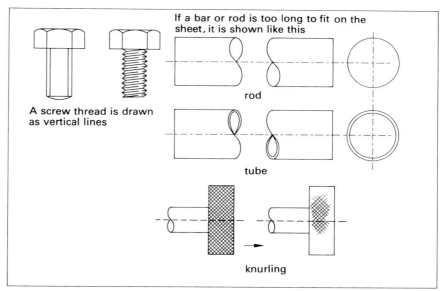

Fig. 1.79   Conventions

If you are in doubt as to what the convention should be for a particular detail, check with the BS 308 recommendations or look in the schools' condensed version of these.

Setting out

The setting out of the drawing sheet is important if all the information is to fit and be in a readable position. The layout of the sheet also helps to present the drawing in the best possible way.

It is normal to draw a narrow border around the edge of the sheet, to act as a frame. A title block is drawn across the bottom of the sheet. Inside this, print the following information:

1. *Title of the drawing* – to explain what the drawings are about; this may be important as sometimes only parts are shown.
2. *Scale of the drawing* – if a measurement is missing the drawing can be checked from the dimension.
3. *Type of projection* – so that parts are viewed the correct way round. (Drawn as a symbol.)
4. *Date drawing done* – it is clear how old the drawing is and if it has since been renewed.
5. *Name of the designer* – if any doubts are raised about the drawing this person can be contacted.
6. *Drawing number* – a working order is then possible and a check as to how many drawings there should be: for example, drawing N°3 may be put as DWG N°3 of 6.

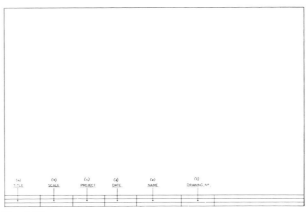

Fig. 1.80

Before the drawing starts, the overall layout of the sheet needs to be planned out. This is so that no details overlap the edges or each other. Use the main sizes of the objects to divide up the sheet space, so that they fit without cramping or wasting areas of paper.

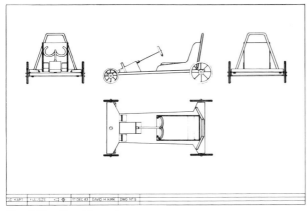

Fig. 1.81   Good layout

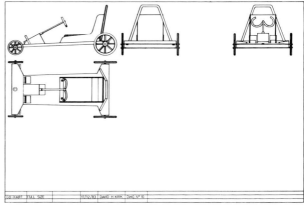

Poor setting out

Why is it important to know the number of design sheets when making an object?

This setting up of the sheet should be used for all the forms of technical drawing, from freehand sketching to working and presentation drawings.

The working drawing can be broken down into two stages:

1 A parts or detail drawing

This is used to explain how each part of an object should be made, giving all the sizes and materials to be used. Each part is numbered. This is further explained in a materials list, stating what the part is, how many are required, what materials to use and the overall sizes. An example is given in Fig. 1.82.

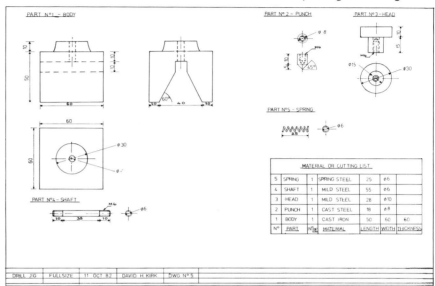

Fig. 1.82   Parts or detail drawing

2 An assembly drawing

This is used to explain how the different parts fit together and in what order. It also gives the total view of the object. This is why pictorial drawing is sometimes used alongside the orthographic. An example is given in Fig. 1.83.

How does the supplying of the parts numbers help with an assembly drawing?

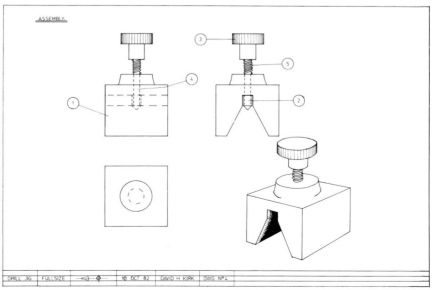

Fig. 1.83   Assembly

The final presentation drawing

Any design needs to have a final realistic drawing if it is to convey to other people what the finished article will look like. This may well be the way the idea is sold – giving its appearance, size, scale, colour and possible uses.

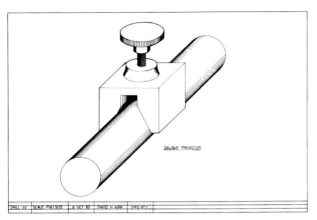

Fig. 1.84 a) Oblique

b) Isometric

The final presentation drawing or drawings can be completed in any of the forms mentioned in the freehand section. The two point perspective is best, because it is able to give the most natural appearance (see Fig. 1.84). This time, however, instruments can be used to help produce the most accurate detailed drawing possible.

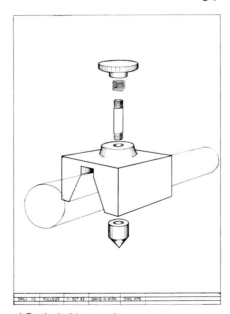

d) Two point perspective

c) Exploded isometric

Why should mistakes not be made at this final stage of design drawing?

Areas of the object can be shown exploded; colour and texture can be used to highlight important detail. From this final drawing it should be possible to decide if the whole idea is practical and suitable for what it is intended. If not, suggestions and modifications can be made at this stage before costly mistakes are made.

32

1 Design

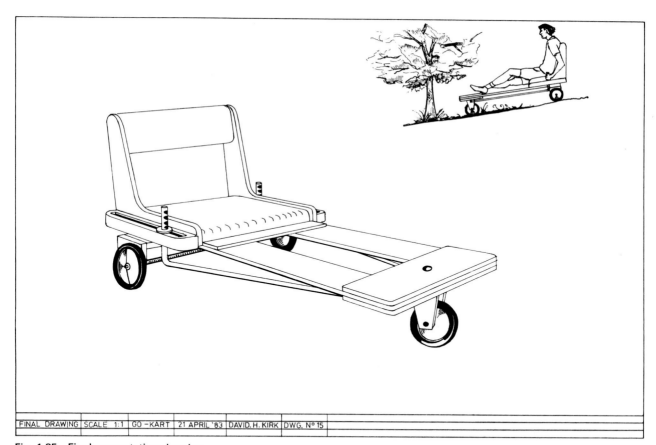

| FINAL DRAWING | SCALE 1:1 | GO-KART | 21 APRIL '83 | DAVID.H.KIRK | DWG. Nº 15 | |

Fig. 1.85   Final presentation drawing

1.6 MODEL MAKING

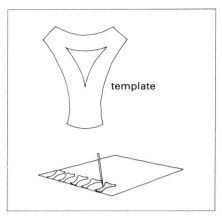

Fig. 1.86   2D model

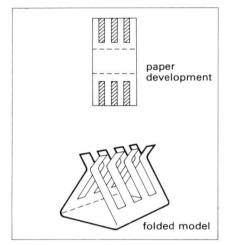

Fig. 1.87   3D model

What form of glue would be best for a paper or card model?

There comes a stage in designing when a drawing is not able to convey the overall effect; this may be scale, size, proportion or working features. It is at this point that a model is used, being able to give a three-dimensional feel to the design. A model should be:
1. simple to construct;
2. able to withstand reasonable handling and testing;
3. give a reasonable impression of the final object;
4. inexpensive.

Paper models

These are the simplest type of model. They are easy to mark out, shape or cut and can be joined with most adhesives at low cost. They do, however, have one major disadvantage: they are not very durable and can easily be damaged.

2D models

This type of model can be used as a pattern or template to help with the marking out. In this way, waste can be reduced by better use of space; time is saved by not having to keep marking out the shape (Fig. 1.86).

3D models

For these to be successful the object has to be drawn first as an unfolded shape. This is normally called a *development*. When this is cut and folded, it will form the model shape (Fig. 1.87). Tabs are sometimes added to help with any gluing.

Card models

These are also a simple method of making a model. Different thicknesses are available in a wide range of colours. They provide greater strength than paper. They are best cut with a modelling knife. When a line is to be folded it is best scored with a blunt tool. The tool is passed alongside a marker. The card will then bend easily along the 'scored' lines (Fig. 1.88).

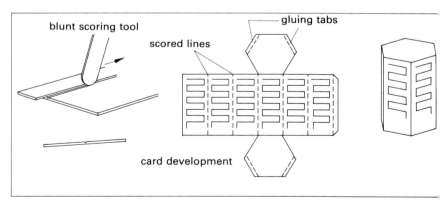

Fig. 1.88

Clay models

Clay provides the ideal modelling material for a difficult shape that has no flat sides and may have irregular curves. It can easily be shaped by hand and worked with fine tools. Parts can be joined together to form a whole shape. When finished, the model is quite durable. The main advantage is that it can be quickly remodelled if found to be unsuitable.

What would you say was the disadvantage of using clay for modelling?

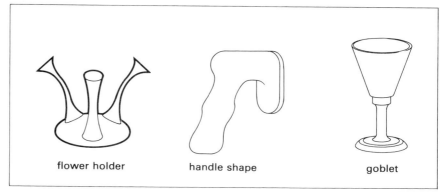

flower holder   handle shape   goblet

Fig. 1.89

Tinplate and wire models

When larger and more substantial models are needed tinplate and wire can be used to represent metal framework and rods. It is also possible to have a simple working model, using the thin wire as a shaft or axle. The tinplate can be cut easily with tinsnips. Then it can be bent or folded. Joining can be done by soft soldering. One disadvantage is that tinplate edges can be dangerous unless they are turned or bent over.

What other tools would you need for making tinplate or wire models?

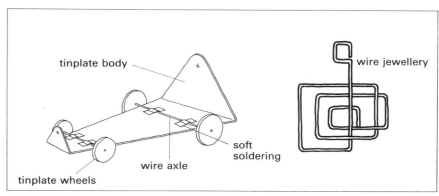

tinplate body

wire jewellery

soft soldering

wire axle

tinplate wheels

Fig. 1.90

Balsa wood models

Balsa wood is used for making larger and more rigid models, such as furniture, bridges, boats, houses. The balsa is soft and easily shaped. It has the advantage that it can be worked with light tools such as a modelling knife and a fret saw. It joins together quickly when you use balsa cement or an impact adhesive. The main disadvantage is its high cost.

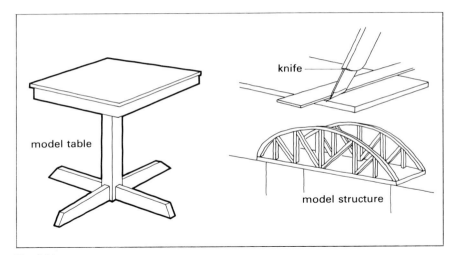

Fig. 1.91

Plastic models

When a model has a large surface area it is sometimes better to use a plastic material. This can be easily heated and bent to the shape required or built up from a number of sections. Sheet material such as polystyrene or acrylic are ideal for heating and forming; expanded polystyrene is ideal for large built-up shapes.

What are the problems with using expanded polystyrene? For example, consider cutting and joining.

Construction kits

These are manufactured modelling kits, made from plastic or metal. They provide an excellent system for building working models. The only disadvantage is the high cost of building up a comprehensive kit.

These then are the many different materials and systems. They can be used as they are or combined to gain the best out of each method. What system to use will depend on the design and what information the model has to convey; for example, does it have to be tested, and if so, is it tested to destruction?

1.7 ERGONOMICS

It is essential to first understand the meaning of this relatively new word – ergonomics. It can be defined as the scientific study of the relationship between people and their living and working environment. It can include the tools, materials and equipment that are used.

The study of ergonomics helps the designer in a number of ways:

1. **Body size (anthropometry)**
   By measuring a large number of people who will be involved in using the final design work, it is possible to obtain the approximate sizes. The designer can discover what the maximum or minimum size will be, and what the average will be. The design can be made to fit as wide a range as possible. The measurements could be for a small area such as a hand or for the whole body. They could also be for a particular group of people e.g. nurses, old age pensioners.

A person working at a desk.

A child riding a bicycle.

Someone cooking in a kitchen.

Fig. 1.92

What body positions and what degrees of movement would you need to study for a person driving a car?

Fig. 1.93 Body size

2. Body movement (anatomy)

By placing people in a given situation, it is possible to note the amount of movement that can be made without discomfort. This provides information about the limits that are possible and the available space around.

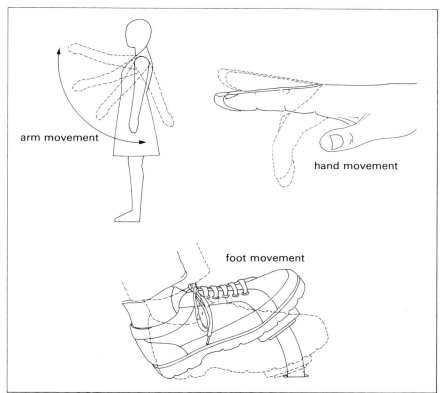

arm movement

hand movement

foot movement

Fig. 1.94 Body movements

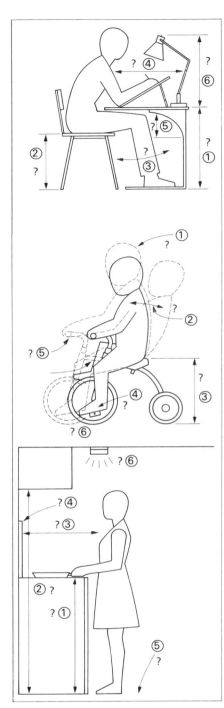

Fig. 1.95

Many people complain that kitchens are badly designed. Can you suggest why?

3. Body conditions (environment)

The surrounding conditions can be checked, to see if they are to prove harmful to the user. This could be smell, noise, light, heat, cold etc. For example, if we design a machine that emits a high-pitched noise while working, the noise could be irritating and harmful to other people working there. The study information can be used by the designer to correct previously bad conditions.

If we return to the examples on page 37, we can see what factors need study to help the designer.

A person working at a desk

We would need to know some of the following details:
1. What is the best height for the desk, giving the most comfortable working position?
2. What height should the chair be for working at the desk, giving both comfort and support?
3. In what position would the person's legs be when sitting at the desk?
4. How wide should the desk be, so that most items can be reached?
5. What is the limit for the desk drawers?
6. What is the best height for the desk light?

A child riding a bicycle

The following details may be needed:
1. What age child is to use the bicycle? Is it a boy or a girl?
2. What is the most comfortable position for riding?
3. How far should the seat be from the ground?
4. What distance should the pedals be from the ground?
5. What shape should the handles be for a good grip?
6. What colour would attract attention?

Someone cooking in a kitchen

Perhaps some of the following would need study:
1. What is the best height for the working surfaces e.g. kitchen sink, cooker, work tops?
2. How high can the wall cupboards be, whilst being within reach?
3. How wide should the worktops be, so that items can be reached?
4. In what position should the cooker controls be, so that they can be read and operated?
5. What would be the best type of safe floor covering?
6. How should the kitchen be lit, to provide the best working light?

How can we use ergonomics – all the information collected – on a piece of design work? Let us take a simple example: to design a method of pulling open a wooden drawer.

The hand will be the most useful part of the body, so we need to study this in some detail. We need to know who is to use the drawer. For example, if it is a kitchen drawer, it may be used by people young and old, male and female. If it is a playschool desk, it may be used by small children about 3 to 5 years old.

Let us assume that the drawer is for a kitchen unit, which will need one hand to open it. We can now study the shape and size of people's hands between the ages of 18 and 70. We can also study the amount of movement possible.

Now look at the best position for pulling with a hand: either the palm facing upwards or downwards. This will need some research or experiment.

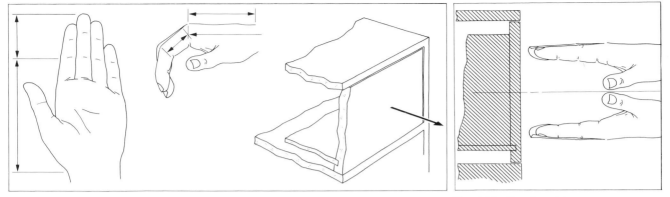

Fig. 1.96

Fig. 1.97   Hand position

Why should fingernails present a problem?

Having collected your information, start to look at the design problem. The first idea could be to use a single hole and to pull the drawer open with one finger. From our research, we can work out the size needed for the hole. But which finger will be the strongest? The hole must allow the finger to bend slightly, in order to make it possible to exert a pull. Sharp edges could be a problem: the shaping of the hole must fit the finger.

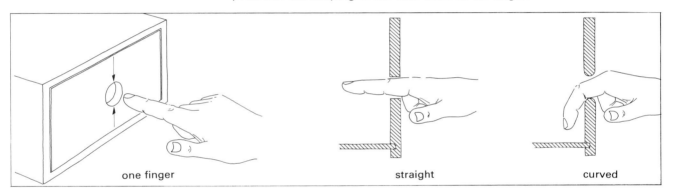

one finger   straight   curved

Fig. 1.98

Which finger would you think was the strongest?

How do you think the amount of movement would differ as the user gets older?

Any finger system would have very limited strength, so the whole hand must be better. If we increase the size of the hole to allow the whole hand to pass through we could arrive at a slot shape. Once again the sharp corners must be removed to allow the hand to pass and bend.

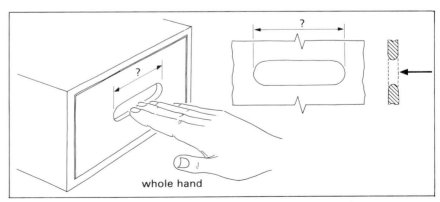

whole hand

Fig. 1.99   Hand slot

The problem with a hole or slot is that it will also allow dirt and dust to pass into the drawer. We could shape the top or the bottom of the drawer front. Or a shallow insert could be used to take the tips of the fingers (Fig. 1.100). Our research will tell us the size of the recess for the fingers ¬ and possible angles.

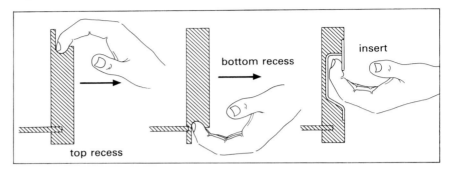

Fig. 1.100   Finger recess

It may be that a shallow recess is uncomfortable for some people, so try a knob, a handle or a ring. This time the study will prove useful as to what type of grip is best and what sizes are needed. Check the amount of space we need to allow between the front of the drawer and the grip so that the fingers can pass easily (Fig. 1.101).

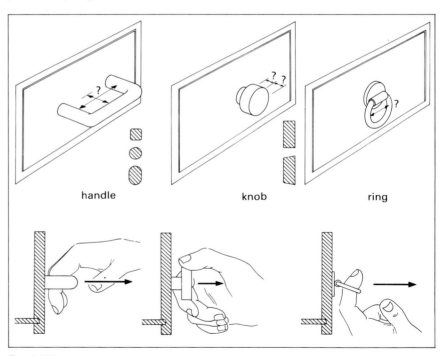

Fig. 1.101

Can you suggest what areas would need to be studied for the design of a shopping trolley?

In all the methods mentioned above, the study information has given a general guideline. It can also be used in the selection of material. The designer works around the information to produce his or her design. However, the final test of the object or work must be when it is used. This is why a model or prototype is a valuable aid to the working properties of the design.

We have now looked at design; the many methods that can be used in its presentation. The next stage is to see how they come together to help solve three-dimensional problems.

Three-dimensional or practical design can be divided into two main areas: *aesthetic design* and *functional design*.

Aesthetic design

In what ways would this area of design affect the motor car?

With this type of design problem the major part of the work will be the final look or appearance of the object. This will be developed from lines, shapes, forms, colour, texture etc. For example, the problem could be to produce an award trophy for a tennis tournament — the appearance will play an important part in the design. Another example could be that an item is beginning to look out of date. Industry does this a great deal to help resell its products in such things as electrical goods, cars, garden tools, kitchen equipment. This is said to be **industrial design**.

Functional design

What parts of a passenger aircraft would be functional, and which would be aesthetic?

In this type of problem the final designed object has to fulfil a purpose; for example, it may be hold a cup or move a door. The design will be developed out of such things as weight, strength, material (wood, metal or plastic). For example, if a large number of bricks have to be pushed along the ground by hand, the problem is very functional: What material should be used? How can they be moved? Is there to be some aid to the pushing? If the final design does not fulfil these points it will have failed. Industry uses functional design for such things as car engines, machines, electrical circuits, civil engineering. This is said to be **engineering design**.

Most of the work we encounter in school will involve both aesthetic and functional design. How much each part plays in the problem will depend very much on what is to be the final use. For example, if we are asked to solve the problem of loose toothbrushes in the bathroom, a simple functional item could be a block of wood with holes screwed to the wall — yet few homes would want such an object. If, however, the block was given a more attractive appearance with shape, colour and texture, a very different view will be taken. When designing we must not forget to consider both these areas and the parts they play in helping to solve problems.

Design example — watch support

Let us first look at how a design problem or project starts. It can arise from either an *observed problem* or a *given problem*. An example of an observed problem could be when an old person is seen to have problems turning a key in a door. An example of a given problem could be supplied by a customer who is willing to pay you for solving his or her problem of carrying records.

Before you start you must be clear about what the problem really is, and what you are being asked to design. This is very important as it will set the limits in which you have to work. To make this clear you should always write out a short introduction about the problem. This is called the **design brief**.

A problem could be that a large number of pupils in a school are taking examinations in a hall. The wall clock is in an awkward position, being behind many of the candidates. As time plays an important part in any examination, some additional aid must be used. One suggestion is that each pupil is given a device that can hold his or her own watch, in a handy position on the table or desk in front of them. The watch can be used as a guide to the time, while the main hall clock will be the overall timekeeper. The final device, however, must not interfere too much with the paperwork and notes on the desk.

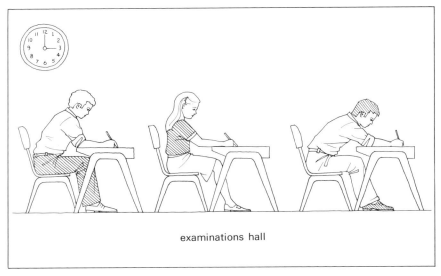

examinations hall

Fig. 1.102   Design problem

This then is the problem, so the design brief could be written down as follows:
To design a small watch support for a candidate in an examination, so that the time can be noted without interfering with the examination papers on his or her desk.

We now have the limits in which to work. The next stage is to think out or *analyse* the problem, by considering all the contributory factors. These include who will use it, where it will be used, how it will be used, what material would be suitable, what type of finish should be used, how much it is to cost, etc. This means that the problem needs to be divided up into parts or areas, so that information can be collected or researched. Outstanding points can be made clear and judgements made, leading to a solution.

If we return to our design problem and see how this can be broken down into parts, it would seem to divide into four main problem areas:
1. the pupil or candidate (numbers, measurements [anthropometric])
2. the watch (details, sizes, etc.)
3. the desk (environment, ergonomics)
4. the support (shape/size/etc.)

We can now deal with each in turn. This is best done by asking yourself questions, before trying to find the answers. These can be in a written or sketch and note form. Our analysis could progress as shown in Table 1.

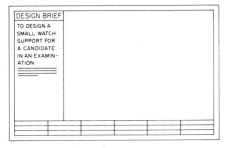

Fig. 1.103   Sheet layout

Research the areas needed for your school.

The pupil or candidate	Answer	Possible research needed
Analysis		
(a) Who are the pupils, boys or girls?	This could be both in our school situation.	Numbers needing the watch support.
(b) Why will it matter if the pupil is a boy or girl?	The size and shape of each watch will vary greatly.	
(c) What is the age of the pupils?	This also could vary, but important exams take place at 16+.	Check age range.
(d) How will this affect the watch?	It will only affect the size of the watch strap (length and width).	The size and shape of pupils' wrists. (*anthropometric data*)
The watch		
(a) What is the approximate size of a boy's or girl's watch?	This will need research to give the correct data.	Measure a range of boys' and girls' watches.
(b) What is the size and material used for watch straps?	Further research into boys' and girls' watches.	Check materials and methods of fastening.
(c) At what distance can the watch face be seen and read?	When worn on the hand it is about 300mm; standing will need some research.	Experiment with watches standing in different positions. (*investigation*)
The desk		
(a) What is the desk top size?	This may vary according to the type used?	Measure the general types available.
(b) What is the maximum space left after all the examination papers are laid out?	This will vary greatly from exam to exam.	Check what is the minimum and maximum paperwork for each examination.
(c) What material is the table top made from?	Again this will vary according to the type.	Check the materials used, slip or non-slip. (thickness)

The support	Answer	Possible research needed
(a) How is the watch to be held? (*functional design*)	By the support, using a block, hook, peg, ring to hold the strap or face.	May need some research into possible ways of holding.
(b) At what height should the support hold the watch? (*functional design*)	This will link up with the reading distance and angle.	Research done under *The watch*.
(c) How is the support to fit on to the desk? (*functional design*)	It could stand, clamp, screw on to the desk, but it must be stable in use.	Check what is possible with the desks.
(d) What sort of appearance should the support have? (*aesthetic design*)	As it is to be on view a great deal it should be pleasant to look at without distracting.	Shapes (natural, geometrical)
(e) What possible material could be used? (*functional and aesthetic*)	It needs to be light and easy to handle, yet able to withstand constant collecting and storing.	Check suitable materials: wood, metal, plastic. (*technology*)
(f) What sort of finish should be used? (*functional and aesthetic*)	Needs to withstand constant handling, so must be tough.	Check suitable finishes: paint, polish, wax, etc. (*technology*)
(g) What safety points need the support have? (*functional*)	It should have no sharp edges, be easy to clean and be stable.	
(h) How difficult should the support be to make? (*functional*)	As a large number is needed, the method of manufacture should be quite simple. Jigs and fixtures may be ideal.	
(i) How much should the support cost? (*functional*)	About 50p (low cost item), due to large numbers needed.	Compare prices of the different materials and working times.
(j) Is the final support to be stacked or stored? (*functional*)	It would seem that it will need to both stack and store.	Types of storage available: boxes, cupboards, trays.

Table 1

If we did not analyse a design problem first, what faults would tend to show up in the solution?

As we develop the analysis, our **first** ideas and possible solutions begin to form from the information. This is now converted into sketch or drawing form, some of which will be impractical, others that can be developed further. This is called the *synthesis* or the comparing of ideas in drawing form. You can use any of the many drawing systems we looked at earlier, such as isometric, perspective or orthographic. At this stage all drawing is done in the quick freehand style. This enables you to express all your ideas.

Synthesis

The synthesis for our problem could be as follows:
Under the support analysis we looked at possible ways of holding the watch. This we can develop further, using geometrical shapes as a design source.

As you can see, notes of explanation start to appear beside the sketches. It is important that all ideas are put down and considered, looking at why it is good or bad. Possible construction and materials also start to be considered. (Turn to the Technology section for help in this area.)

From the holding system we can look at ways it can be supported.

Further areas could be the adjustment of the holding system.

We should now be able to combine the ideas into at least three design solutions: each a possible answer to the problem.

It is at this stage that a model proves to be valuable, and can help us to choose the correct solution without too much effort.

Consider how the support could be clamped to the desk. Draw up a suitable system.

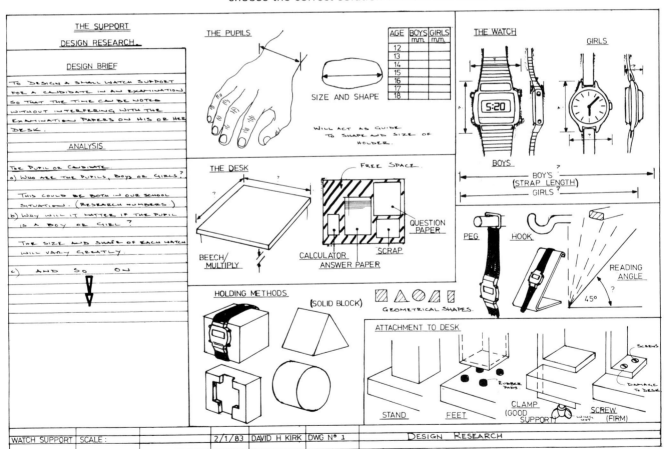

Fig. 1.104

1 Design

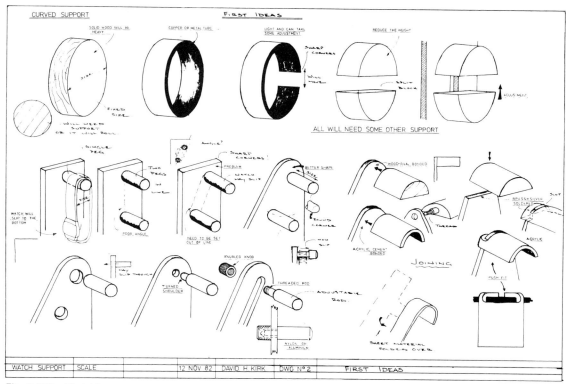

Fig. 1.105   First ideas

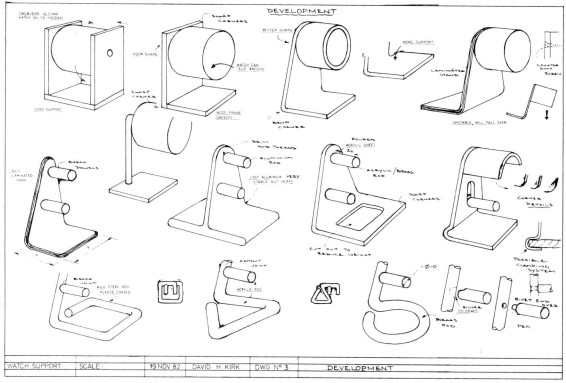

Fig. 1.106   Development of ideas

Solving design problems

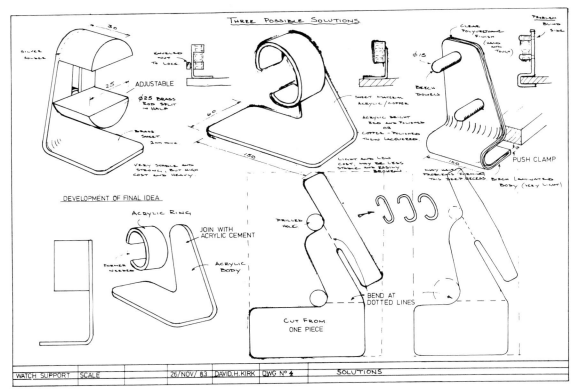

Fig. 1.107 Three possible solutions

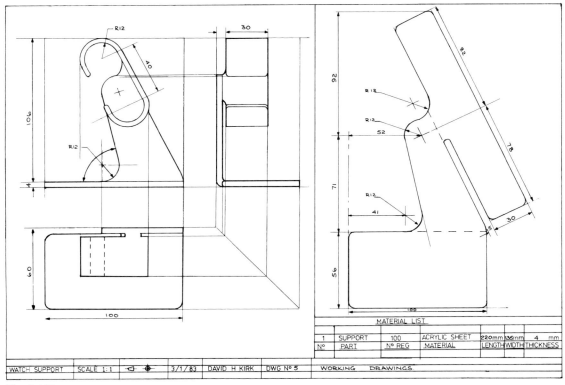

Fig. 1.108

Extra material is usually allowed on some of the cutting list sizes. Can you think why?

Once we have decided upon the final solution, working drawings can be drawn up. These can show both assembly and detail for the final object. We will also need to work out a material or cutting list, so that it can be prepared or ordered ready for making up.

To complete the design we can now draw the final presentation drawing (Fig. 1.109).

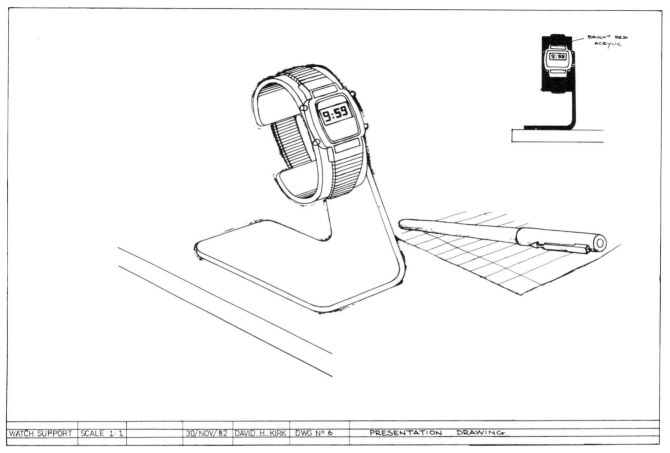

WATCH SUPPORT	SCALE 1:1		30/NOV/82	DAVID. H. KIRK	DWG Nº 6	PRESENTATION DRAWING.

Fig. 1.109

Realisation

Once the design is finalised, with all the working drawings complete, the practical work can start. First make up a scale model. In this way, very simple checks and tests can be carried out: for example, from our design piece it would be possible to make up a simple card. Sizes could be checked, ways of forming the shape, trying the watch in position, angles etc. Minor changes or modifications can be made without wasting materials or time and energy.

The next stage is to plan out how the object is to be made, and in what order the processes should take place. Snags can be thought out before mistakes are made: for example, should the piece of acrylic sheet shown in Fig. 1.110, be cut out before or after bending? For our design a planning list could be:

1. Cut out a piece of acrylic to the overall size.
2. Square up the material, with a file and scraper.
3. Mark out the design shape with a chinagraph pencil.
4. Remove the waste material by first drilling a ⌀12 hole, then cutting down with a hacksaw.

Can you complete the list for making up the support?

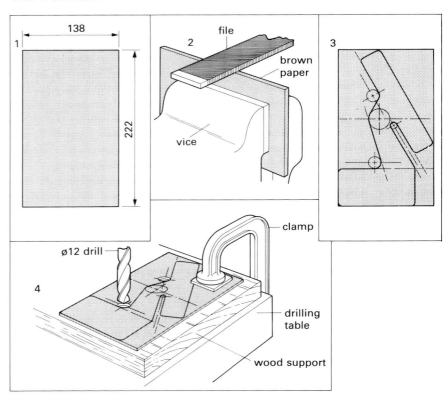

Fig. 1.110   Stages of planning (production)

The practical work can now start and any minor problems or modifications in the making should be carefully noted for future use.

On completion, the prototype can be tried out or tested and from this we can determine how successful the design has been. It is only after this that we can start to think in terms of producing several — mass production. We need to consider both the aesthetic look of the object and the functional working of the object. Give a brief report on the good or bad points of the design. This is called a *critical evaluation*.

If we look again at our example, the critical evaluation could be as follows.

Possible evaluation report – for watch support

Aesthetic viewpoint – the overall appearance seemed to work quite well, with a shape that blended with the watch and strap. However, the vertical section lacked interest being rather flat and dull. It should be possible to improve this by cutting away sections to give a more open design. The bright colour chosen (red) tended to distract the eye from the watch face; perhaps a quiet colour (e.g. pale blue) would be more suitable.

Functional viewpoint – the holder held the watch well, allowing it to be removed quite easily and at a good viewing angle. It does, however, only fit one type of watch, so some form of adjustment is needed to overcome this problem and give the support wider use. Being made in acrylic helped to produce a light and colourful object that could be easily cleaned. Being very light the support did tend to move rather easily on the desk, so could be pushed or knocked over with little effort. This could be overcome by adding brass feet for extra weight, without losing its overall appearance. When the support is stacked it takes up a lot of space and tends to be rather awkward to handle. It may be possible to design the support so that it folds flat when not in use. This, however, will add to the cost and time of production.

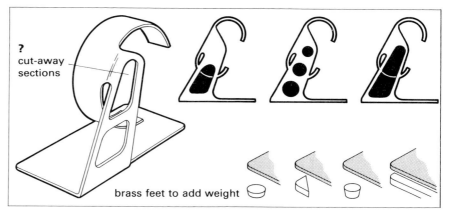

Fig. 1.111

This final part of the design project is very important to the designer if his or her work is to improve and progress. From it we can see that we have arrived at only one solution and that many more are possible.

From our watch stand example, we saw the need for an understanding of materials, construction and possible processes as the design developed. In the example, some simple decisions had been made on these points, but how had they been arrived at and why? Had the correct resources been used?

To see what other possible materials, construction and production techniques could have been used, we need to look at technology.

Part Two

Technology

2.1 PRODUCTION OF METALS

Metals fall into three broad categories:

1. *ferrous* (those composed mainly of iron, with small additions of other substances – e.g. mild steel, tool steel, cast iron)

2. *non-ferrous* (those that contain no iron – e.g. copper, lead, aluminium, tin, zinc)

3. *alloys* (metals that are formed by mixing different metals; they may be ferrous or non-ferrous – e.g. stainless steel [steel & chromium] and high speed steel [steel & tungsten] are ferrous alloys, while brass [copper & zinc] and duralumin [aluminium & copper] are non-ferrous alloys).

The ferrous metals are the most important, as they play such a major part in our modern lives. They are used in industry, agriculture, transport, building, sport and even in the home.

> What things can you think of that are made from some form of steel that fit into these areas: industry, agriculture, transport, building, sport, home?

Ferrous metals

The raw metal is obtained from iron-bearing rocks, which we term as iron ore. These rocks are found in different forms, each type containing a different amount of iron.

Type of ore	% iron content	Colour	Where found
Magnetite	65%	Black	Sweden, USA, USSR
Haematite	Up to 60%	Red-brown	USA, North Spain, North Africa
Limonite	Up to 30%		Sweden, France, Germany

Table 2

In Britain, we have some very small deposits of haematite. Most of the raw material for our steel-making plants has to be imported. To convert the ore into a usable material, it has to go through a number of processes.

The blast furnace

It is the blast furnace that converts the mineral ore into iron. First, the ore is washed, crushed and mixed with coke and limestone. The coke acts as a fuel for the process; the limestone acts as a flux helping to separate the impurities as the process takes place. Together the three parts form the **charge**. On average, 1 metric tonne of pig iron can be produced from 4 tonnes of ore, 1¾ tonnes of coke and 1 tonne of limestone.

The charge is now tipped into the furnace, passing through a valve system which is operated by two bells (see Fig. 2.1). These allow the charge to drop into the furnace, without letting out the heat. Inside, the heat drives off moisture from the ore. As the charge slips down the furnace, the limestone starts to decompose and the iron and the impurities start to separate. Some of the impurities form into a liquid waste called **slag**. The heavy liquid iron falls to the bottom of the furnace, with the lighter slag floating on top. The process is continuous; the slag and the iron are periodically drained or tapped off. In this form, the iron is about 90–95% pure and as such has little

> How does the hot air blasted in at the furnace bottom help the smelting process?

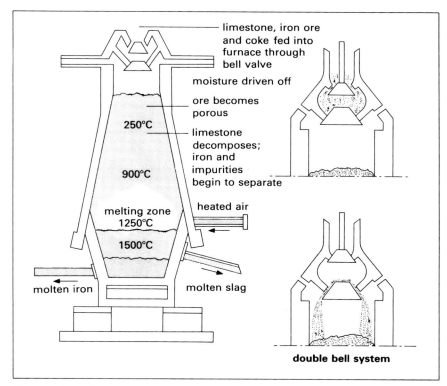

Fig. 2.1 Blast furnace

use. It is brittle and weak. It now has to be refined to convert it into the metals we know: steel and cast iron.

Cast iron

This is made by refining the cold 'pig iron' from the blast furnace in a much smaller furnace called a **cupola**. The process reduces the amount of carbon in the material, as well as controlling elements such as silicon, sulphur and phosphorus. As it has quite a low melting point and flows well when molten, it is used for casting into shapes. Drilling machine bases, tables, lathe bodies and tailstock are all made from cast iron. In a less brittle form – malleable cast iron – it is used for the body shapes of tools such as planes, spokeshaves, and woodwork vices.

Steel

This is made by using hot metal from the blast furnace and mixing it with scrap metal (iron or steel), or just by using scrap on its own. The amounts of material will vary according to the process and the type of steel required. Two main processes are used in Britain: a) basic oxygen furnace; b) electric arc furnace.

Basic oxygen furnace (Fig. 2.2)

This major method of producing steel can make 350 tonnes in 40 minutes. The furnace is like a large drum, which can be tilted. The furnace is tipped forwards and partly filled with scrap metal (30%) and hot metal from the blast furnace (70%). It is returned to its upright position, and a water-cooled oxygen lance is lowered in, stopping just above the metal. High purity oxygen is blown onto the surface of the metal at great speed. The oxygen combines with carbon and other impurities, causing them to burn out of the metal. This is called the **blow**. Lime is added to act as a flux for those

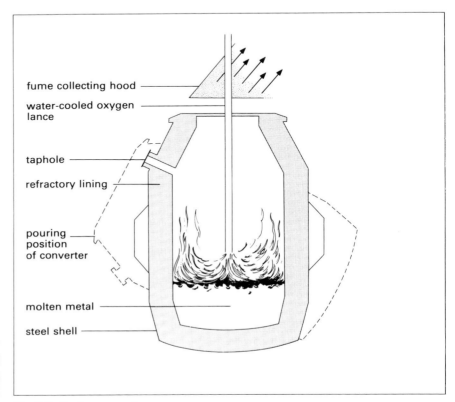

fume collecting hood

water-cooled oxygen lance

taphole

refractory lining

pouring position of converter

molten metal

steel shell

Fig. 2.2   Basic oxygen furnace

Why should this method be good for fuel conservation?

impurities left. This forms a slag on top of the steel. Once the steel is refined and checked, it is poured out of the taphole into ladles. To remove the slag, the furnace has to be tipped upside down.

Electric arc furnace (Fig. 2.3)

This furnace only uses steel scrap. It makes large amounts of general purpose steels or high quality steels. The furnace is shaped like a large kettle, with a spout and a lid. Cold scrap steel is placed inside. Three carbon

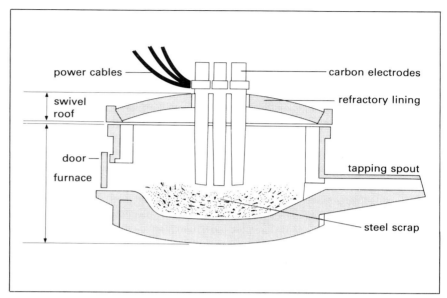

In what way does this furnace help with material conservation?

Fig. 2.3   Electric arc furnace

electrodes in the lid are lowered to just above the scrap. Heat is generated by electric arcs struck between the scrap metal and the electrodes, causing the metal to melt. All the impurities are oxidised from the metal by melting it underneath a covering of lime, fluorspar and iron oxide. These combine to form a slag. The process can produce 150 tonnes of steel in 4 hours. The steel is tapped from the furnace by first tilting it backwards to remove the slag, then forwards to pour the steel from the spout into a ladle. Most alloy steels are made in this way.

Once the steel is made, it is poured from the ladle into shaped moulds. These can be in the form of ingots, large tapered sections of steel or special castings for engineering (e.g. cylinders or frames). The ingot is a convenient way of handling the steel for further shaping, once it has solidified but not cooled.

The further shaping is carried out by one of two methods:

1. By passing the red hot ingot between rollers. It is squeezed into flat slabs or square blooms. These in turn are passed between rollers and from this we obtain our familiar shaped sections of metal: flats, round, bars, sheet etc.

2. The other method is to forge the red hot ingot. This is done by hammering or pressing the metal into a set shape e.g. a car crankshaft.

A new technique being used is to pour the molten steel in a continuous casting system which can form the flat slabs and square blooms without having to handle them as ingots. Slabs and blooms are produced in ready-cut lengths, thereby reducing production costs.

As the steel is rolled hot it has a black oxide finish. This can be seen in the workshop as black mild steel. It is used for less accurate work e.g. forging. For accurate work the steel is cleaned, oiled, re-rolled cold. This produces a very bright finish. We see this in the workshop as bright drawn mild steel.

Can you suggest why it is easier to shape metal while it is in a red hot state?

Production of metals

55

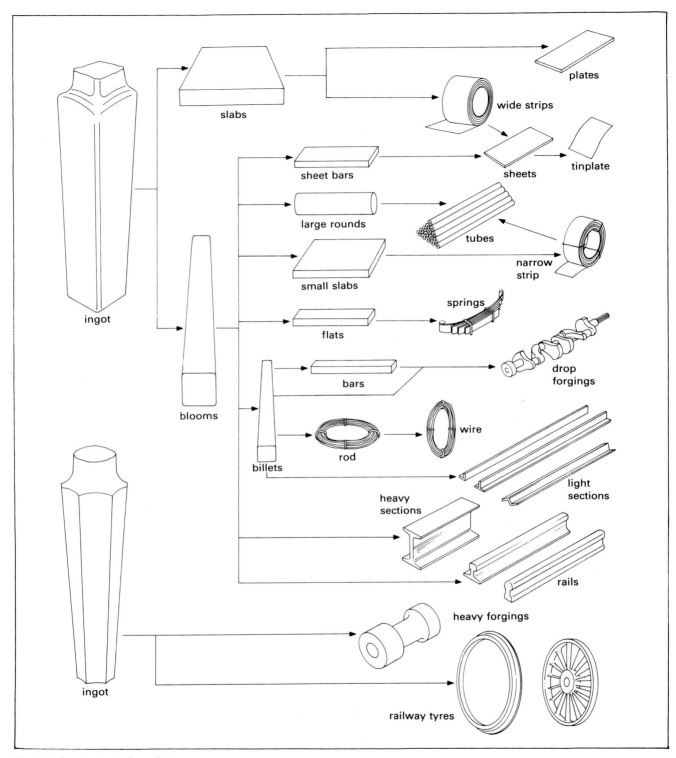

Fig. 2.4 Ingots to steel products

Non-ferrous metals

The major non-ferrous metal is aluminium; its production far exceeds the total annual output of all the other non-ferrous metals put together. The raw material is a rock called bauxite. Unlike iron ore, which can be converted easily by smelting into iron, bauxite has to go through a number of processes before we can obtain aluminium. These processes add to the cost of the final material, as they use great amounts of electricity.

The production has to be done in two stages:

Stage one – crushed bauxite is treated with caustic soda under heat and pressure. The bauxite dissolves and is then filtered to remove impurities. The remaining sodium aluminate liquid is treated and washed to remove any traces of the caustic soda. It is then heated to 1100°C in a rotating tubular kiln known as a calciner. This produces a fine white crystalline powder called **alumina** – aluminium combined with oxygen.

Stage two – the alumina is placed into a shallow steel box or reduction cell, which has a lining of carbon with a flux that is principally *cryolite*. Suspended above the box are a number of carbon rods. The process starts with the molten cryolite dissolving the alumina. A powerful electric current is then passed from the carbon rods (positive anode) through the dissolved liquid to the carbon box lining (negative cathode). This sets up a chemical reaction which separates the aluminium from the oxygen. Molten aluminium collects in the bottom of the box (Fig. 2.4). This is sucked from the box and is about 99% pure.

Why do you think most of the British aluminium production plants are situated in the Scottish Highlands?

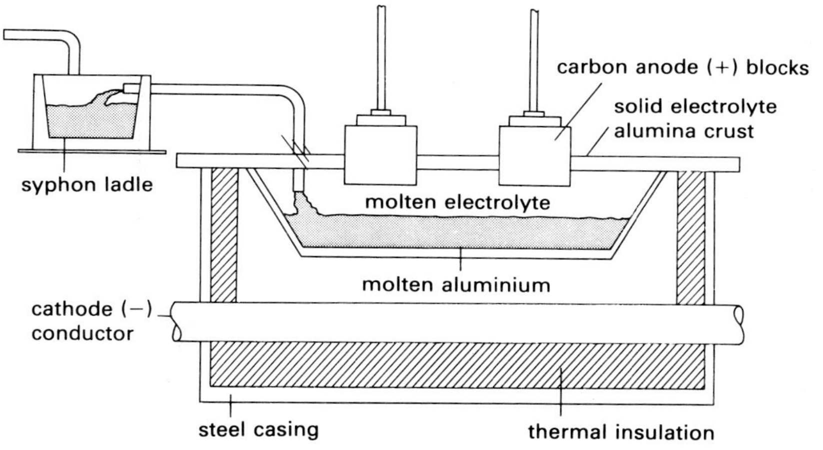

Fig. 2.5   Hall/Heroult process

A large amount of the metal produced is used in this pure form, but a major proportion is used in alloyed forms. Such metals as copper, magnesium and manganese are added to improve its properties of hardness and strength. Like steel, the aluminium is cast into ingots for further shaping. The many different forms we see are: rolled sheet, strip, foil, extruded bars, rods, drawn tubes, wire, stampings etc. It can be in cast form and is even used in paint.

2.2 FERROUS AND NON-FERROUS METALS AND THEIR ALLOYS

Metal	Composition	Melting point	Properties
Mild steel	iron, with 0.25% carbon	1600–1800°C	Malleable and ductile metal that rusts easily, but has good strength
High carbon steel (tool or cast steel)	iron with 0.7%–1.5% carbon	1800–3400°C	Less malleable and ductile, but can be hardened and tempered
Cast iron	iron with 3.5% carbon	1240°C	Very brittle with hard surface skin; strong under compression; rusts quite slowly
High speed steel	carbon steel with 18% tungsten	varies according to content	Self-hardening and will retain this at red heat
Stainless steel	carbon steel with about 12% chromium	varies according to content	Hard and tough; high resistance to wear and corrosion
Aluminium	pure metal	658°C	Very light, soft and ductile; good resistance to corrosion
Duralumin	aluminium with 4% copper, manganese and magnesium	varies	Nearly as strong as mild steel, but ⅓ the weight; age hardens and is susceptible to corrosion over period of time
Copper	pure metal	1085°C	Very malleable and ductile; good conductor of heat and electricity; resists corrosion
Gilding metal	copper with 20% zinc	varies	Stronger than copper, but malleable and ductile; has rich golden colour
Brass (English Standard)	copper with 35% zinc	varies	Quite strong, but ductile
Bronze	copper with 10% tin	varies	Strong and tough; resists corrosion well; good wearing properties
Lead	pure metal	327°C	Heavy but very soft; malleable; resists corrosion by water or acid

Working qualities	Uses	Metal
Easy metal to work – files, saws, drills, bends well; can be easily joined by soldering, brazing and welding	General engineering work – in sheet, rod, bar, angle, tube form; also used for nails, screws, bolts, nuts	*Mild steel*
Difficult to file and cut, but can be easily joined by soldering or brazing	Hand tools – saws, chisels, punches, screwdrivers, files; also springs and gauges	*High carbon steel*
Once through hard skin, metal works quite well – cannot be forged and does not haze or weld easily	Vice and machine bodies, cylinder blocks	*Cast iron*
Once hard can only be shaped with a grindstone	Machine and drill lathe tools, milling cutters	*High speed steel*
Difficult to work, file or cut; but can be soldered and brazed	Cutlery, dishes, furniture, frames, jewellery	*Stainless steel*
Works well – can be cut, sawn, bent, cast easily; can be polished to high shine	Kitchen and cooking items, engine parts, foil etc.	*Aluminium*
Works well if it is annealed first	Used when strength and light weight required: aircraft parts, pulleys, belts, screws	*Duralumin*
Very good, can be shaped or bent easily; solders and brazes well; polishes to a high	Water pipes, electrical work, decorative work	*Copper*
Very good, can easily be soldered and brazed	Architectural, metalwork, jewellery	*Gilding metal*
Shapes and bends easily, but hardens quickly; can be joined easily; polishes well	Castings, plumbing fittings, fittings, screws, decorative work	*Brass* (English Standard)
Casts and machines well	Bearings, gears, machine parts, ship fittings	*Bronze*
Cuts and works easily cold; casts well	Plumbing work, roof covering, containers	*Lead*

Table 3

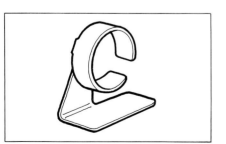

Fig. 2.6

If we return to our design example (Fig. 2.6), the 'watch stand', we can see from Table 3 that **aluminium** (very light, ductile, easily worked) and **gilding metal** (stronger than copper, but malleable with excellent colour) could have been used.

Ferrous and non-ferrous metals and their alloys

Current available forms and sizes of metal

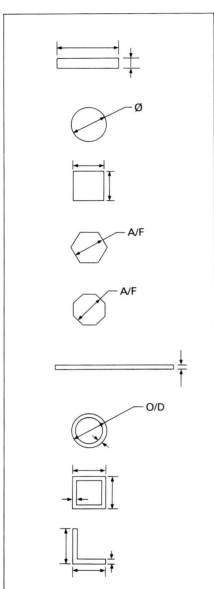

Flat strip or bar	1.5 × 12	3 × 10	3 × 25	5 × 20	6 × 12	6 × 40
	1.5 × 20	3 × 12	3 × 32	5 × 25	6 × 20	6 × 50
	1.5 × 25	3 × 16	3 × 40	5 × 40	6 × 25	
	1.5 × 40	3 × 20	3 × 50	5 × 50	6 × 32	

Round rod ⌀ 3, 4, 5, 6, 8, 10, 12, 16, 20, 25, 32, 40, 50

Square rod 6, 8, 10, 12, 16, 20, 22mm square

Hexagonal rod 6, 8, 10, 12, 16, 20, 25mm across flats (A/F)

Octagonal rod 6, 8, 10, 12, 16, 20, 25mm across flats (A/F)

Sheets 1800mm × 900mm, 1200mm × 600mm × 0.65, 0.80, 0.95, 1.2, 1.6, 2.0, 2.5, 3.0mm thick

Round tube 5, 6, 8, 10mm O/D × 0.95; 12, 16, 20mm O/D × 1.2; 25, 32, 40mm O/D × 1.6
(O/D is the Outside Diameter, the second figure is the tube wall thickness.)

Square tube 12, 16mm square × 1.2; 20, 25mm square × 1.6

Angle equal 12 × 12 × 1.5; 20 × 20 × 1.5; 20 × 20 × 3; 25 × 25 × 3mm

These are just some of the very many forms and sizes available. Care should be taken as many of the sizes given are not true metric sizes – many manufacturers are still producing materials in the old imperial system. Always check that the material you intend to use is available and is the size stated.

Fig. 2.7

2.3 STRUCTURE OF METALS

If the designer or craftsman/woman is to get the maximum use from metals, he or she must fully understand the structure and properties they possess (see Table 3). You need to know how these may be changed or controlled in certain ways. For example, is it possible to make a hard metal soft so that it may be bent? Or is it possible to make a soft metal hard so that it will not bend?

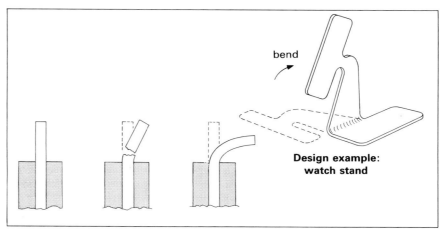

Fig. 2.8

We must start with the inner structure of metals known as the **atomic structure**, to see how they are built up. All metals are composed of millions of atoms, so small that they cannot be seen even with the most powerful microscope. The tiny atoms join together in regular geometrical patterns to form crystals. The patterns are called the **lattice structures**, and each metal has a known type. For aluminium, copper and lead the atoms are spaced out in rows at right angles to each other. This forms millions of tiny cubes, with the atoms at each corner and another in the centre of each cube face. This is called a **face centred cubic** crystal (Fig. 2.9).

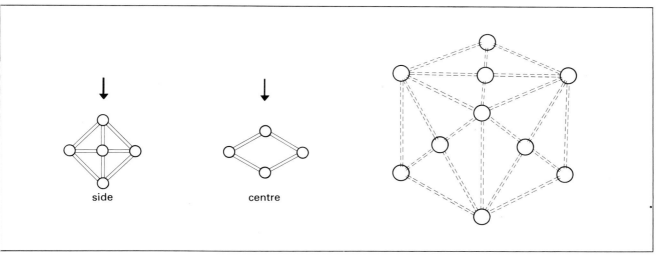

Fig. 2.9   Face centred cubic crystal

Structure of metals

Why do you think the body
centred cubic is stronger than the
face centred cubic?

A similar cubic pattern is found in metals such as iron, tungsten and vanadium. There is a single atom at the centre of the cube. This is called a **body centred cubic** crystal (Fig. 2.10).

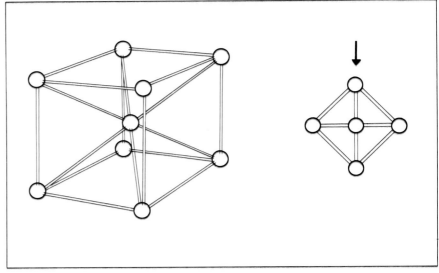

Fig. 2.10   Body centred cubic crystal

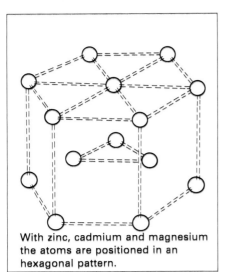

With zinc, cadmium and magnesium the atoms are positioned in an hexagonal pattern.

Fig. 2.11

Look at a piece of galvanised steel
(mild steel with a very thin coating
of zinc). It is possible to see the
large zinc grains with the naked
eye.

Iron is an important metal because its structure changes when it is heated. At normal room temperature it is in the form of the body centred cubic, but when heated to 906°C the atoms re-form into a face centred cubic; while at the higher temperature of 1400°C they form back into body centred cubic. The reverse takes place on slow cooling.

This simple change of structure plays a very important role when iron and carbon are mixed to form steel. It gives the designer the opportunity to make the metal hard or soft, depending on which state the metal is in. This is because in the face centred cubic form, iron can absorb carbon.

These are some of the many different lattice structures that exist in metals. We will see later how they combine together to form metal alloys.

How the structure is formed

This starts to form when the metal begins to cool after being in a liquid or molten state. At various points within the molten metal, the tiny atoms start to join together to form minute crystals. These begin to grow in all directions, in a tree-like formation known as **dendrites**. As the dendrite growths meet, they start to fill in the spaces between the branches until the grains of solid metal are formed.

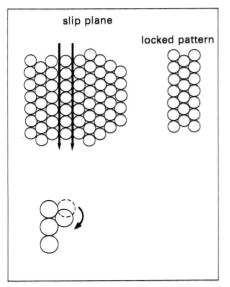

Fig. 2.13   Dislocations

Fig. 2.12

Grain weakness

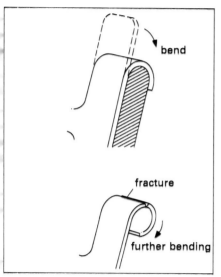

Fig. 2.14 Work hardening

As each metal grain grows, the pattern is not always perfect in its lattice structure. Flaws or faults start to occur, caused by interruptions in the pattern. These are called **dislocations** and are the sources of weakness within the grains. This is due to atoms being out of line with each other and slipping if some force is applied. Once atoms slip they can re-settle into a more regular pattern. This locking of atoms makes the metal much harder and stronger. It is by using these faults that we can cut, bend, draw and hammer metal into different shapes.

If we use a piece of copper for our watch stand, the grains of copper are forced to change shape as we form the bends. The grains move into the curves and become hard (Fig. 2.14). This is called **work hardening**. If further bending takes place the work could fracture or break because the grains are unable to move.

It follows that metals with a small grain structure will be quite strong, having small slip planes; while large grains with large slip planes will produce a weak material. We will see later how the rate of cooling a metal can control the size of the grains, giving a weak or a strong metal.

What is the guide which is used to show the change in temperature when heating metal?

Alloys

We have seen how the pure metals form into lattice patterns, but what happens when two very different metals are mixed together to form an alloy? Let us take brass, which is made up of copper and zinc, as an example. Both copper and zinc have different crystal structures; in addition to this, zinc atoms are 13% larger than copper atoms. When copper takes up the major part of the metal, the lattice structure takes the face centred shape, with the zinc atoms having to fit into the system. This means that one zinc atom replaces a copper atom in the structure. Being much larger, the zinc atom causes the structure to become distorted. This makes it much more difficult for the atoms to slip over each other, resulting in a much stronger metal. The alloy formed with less than 36% zinc is quite workable but is much stronger than copper or zinc on their own. This is known as **gilding metal** or **cartridge brass**. It is used in containers and door fittings.

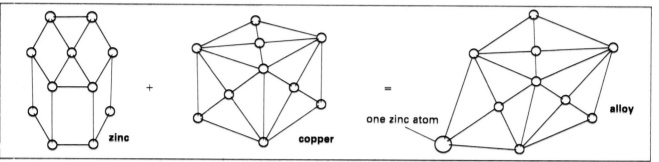

Fig. 2.15 Distorted brass lattice pattern

If a sheet of aluminium is to be bent into our watch stand shape, what size should the grain structure be: large or small?

If more zinc is added to the alloy, the structure gets more and more distorted until, at 36%, another form of lattice develops which is body centred. This forms a much harder and stronger metal, which we know as **naval brass** or **muntz metal**. It is used for fittings on boats and for hot water central heating.

When metals join together in this way they are said to be in **solid solution**.

We have now looked at the simple outline of the structure of metals, how they are built up, and how working them can alter their properties.

Elementary properties of metals

When you are choosing a metal for a design problem or particular function, it will have to possess certain qualities for the work to succeed. It may be that it needs to be hard but light; it may need to withstand high temperatures and to bend easily; and so on. All these details are called *properties* and can be listed as follows:

Colour – will play an important part if the work is to be decorative. It can also be used as a way of identifying metals quickly; for example, copper is reddish-brown, brass is yellow. Some metals, however, are impossible to tell apart because they are so similar; for example, mild steel and tool steel.

Melting point – each metal or alloy has a different temperature at which it will change from a solid to a liquid form. This could be used to advantage in a design e.g. a fire alarm when a low melting metal (such as bismuth) is needed to set off the sprinklers.

Weight – each metal has a known weight. This could be a vital factor on a design; for example, if a piece of work has to be weighted down without too much bulk, which metal could be used? The answer is lead, because it is the heaviest.

> What colour would you use to describe aluminium?

Facts that relate to the working conditions of a metal are called **mechanical properties**. These are as follows:

Strength – can be in three different forms:
1. tensile strength – the metal's ability to resist stretching;
2. compressive strength – the metal's ability to resist squashing;
3. shear strength – the metal's ability to resist being parted.

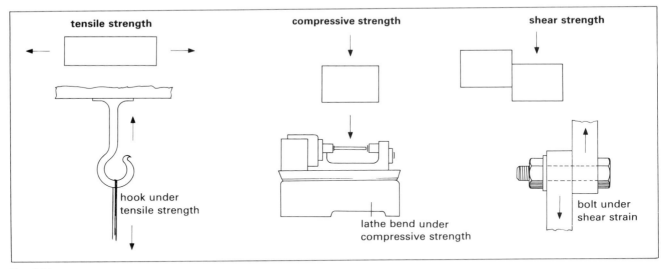

Fig. 2.16

> Choose a metal for each of the mechanical properties listed.

Hardness – the resistance a metal offers to being scratched, worn or cut.
Toughness – the ability to withstand a sudden blow or shock load.
Brittleness (opposite to toughness) – the metal breaks easily with a sharp blow.
Ductility – the ability to be stretched without breaking.
Malleability – a property that allows the metal to be hammered or rolled into shape without breaking.
Conductivity – the ability to conduct heat or electricity.

What properties would be needed for a metal to make up our watch stand example?

Corrosion – the ability to resist corrosion by a chemical action.

How can these properties of metals be checked, so that a mistake is not made? There are two methods: a) simple workshop tests; b) mechanical testing.

Simple workshop tests

These are very simple tests carried out in the workshop, using normal equipment such as the vice, hammer, hacksaw, brazing hearth etc. The test may be to determine the hardness or toughness of a metal or to distinguish one metal from another. For example, if we have two rods of the same size, we can test to find the metals from which each is made. A simple test would be to heat them both to cherry red and to quench in water. Each is then placed in a vice in turn and hit with a hammer. Mild steel will bend, while tool steel will break as it is very brittle. If both rods bend we have two pieces of mild steel. This simple test (Fig. 2.17) has also shown us which metal is malleable and which is brittle.

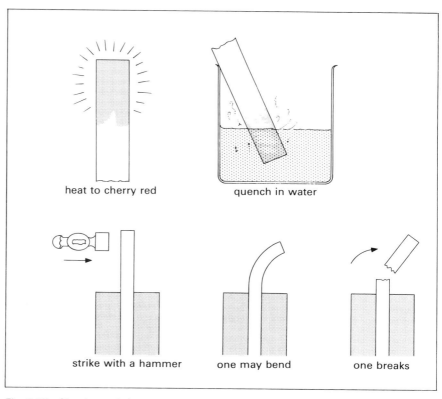

heat to cherry red   quench in water

strike with a hammer   one may bend   one breaks

Fig. 2.17 Simple workshop test

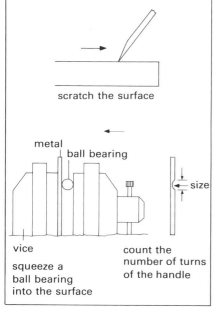

scratch the surface

metal   ball bearing

size

vice

squeeze a ball bearing into the surface

count the number of turns of the handle

Fig. 2.18

Can you think of other simple ways of testing the other properties?

Hardness can be tested by scratching the metal surface or by squeezing a ball bearing into the surface using a vice. In this way we can get a relative hardness. It won't work at all if the metal is harder than the ball bearing. However, if we are comparing different metals, the number of turns of the vice handle will act as a useful guide (Fig. 2.18).

All workshop tests can only be a very general guide to the properties; for more accurate data the tests must be done in a laboratory with special testing machines. The results can be checked with a microscope to very fine limits.

Properties and testing

Mechanical testing

This is carried out for each of the main properties – strength, hardness and toughness.

The tensile test

Can you think of an example when it would be important to know the maximum tensile strength and the final breaking point?

This is the most common test for metals, giving the strength and some idea of the metal's ductility. Sample test pieces are prepared, as shown in Fig. 2.19. Each piece in turn is gripped in a testing machine, and slowly stretched until they break. From the overall results it can be determined how much load the metal can stand before it breaks. It also shows how far the metal can be stretched. The details are normally drawn up in graph form.

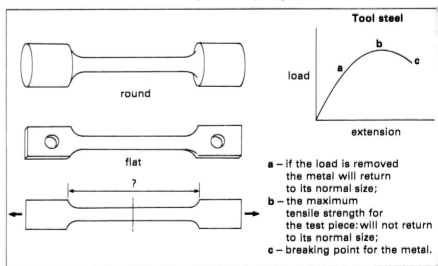

a – if the load is removed the metal will return to its normal size;
b – the maximum tensile strength for the test piece: will not return to its normal size;
c – breaking point for the metal.

Fig. 2.19   Tensile test

The hardness test

Try out the simple workshop test using a ball bearing and see what result you get from a piece of mild steel.

Three different types of test are used in Britain, but all use the principle of forcing a harder object into the surface of the test metal.

Brinell test – a Ø10 hardened steel ball is forced into the surface by a set load. The hardness of the metal is judged by the diameter of the indentation. The hardness is expressed as a number. Problems arise when the metal is so hard that the ball itself becomes deformed.

Vickers test – a very small diamond, pyramid-shaped tool is used to make an indentation. The two diagonals of this are measured and averaged out to give the degree of hardness.

Rockwell test – a very rapid form of testing, using a diamond of a steel ball. The main difference is that the testing machine automatically measures the depth of the indentation: a) under a small load; b) under a large load.

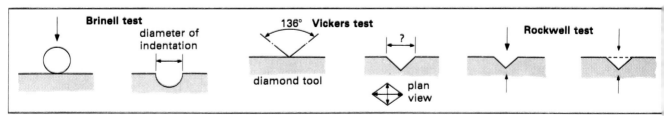

Fig. 2.20   Hardness tests

Toughness testing

It was stated earlier that toughness is the metal's ability to withstand sudden blows. To test this property, a sample piece of metal 10mm square is notched and held in a vice. A sharp blow is applied by a swinging weight.

Izod test – with this test the sample piece is held in a vertical position. A loaded pendulum is released from a set height to give the blow or impact. How far the pendulum swings past after hitting the sample is the guide to how much energy is absorbed. This tells us the toughness of the metal.

Charpy test – a similar test; only this time the sample piece is set in a horizontal position (see Fig. 2.22).

These are just some of the industrial methods of testing metals.

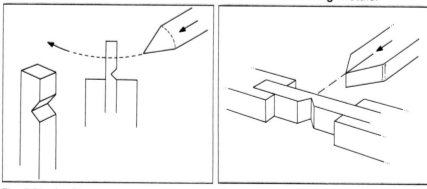

Fig. 2.21   Izod test   Fig. 2.22   Charpy test

2.5 HEAT TREATMENT OF METALS

Earlier we looked at how the grains could move along their slip planes, making them harder and flatter. This may happen after a process such as bending or hammering, and is called **work hardening**. It may be that the material (e.g. duralumin) gets harder with *age*. It is also possible to re-shape the grains by **heating** or **re-crystallisation**. All metals are able to re-crystallise; some more than others. For example, lead can re-crystallise at room temperature. It can be hammered or squeezed. It is very workable because it stays in a soft state. After hammering or squeezing, the crystals re-form – with their slip planes.

Annealing

Most metals need some form of heat to help the grain re-form. This is called annealing. If this is not done and the metal is subjected to working forces (e.g. hammering, bending), the metal will start cracking and breaking up.

Try this with a small piece of sheet aluminium, bending it back and forth while it is held in a vice.

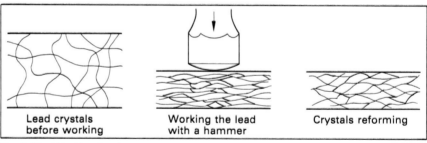

Lead crystals   Working the lead   Crystals reforming
before working   with a hammer

Fig. 2.23   Working lead

Ferrous metals

It is the steels in the workshop that we normally need to anneal, before or after working. Heat the metal to cherry red (about 725°C), then place it in sand so that it can cool very slowly. In this way, large coarse grains are formed, giving a soft workable metal.

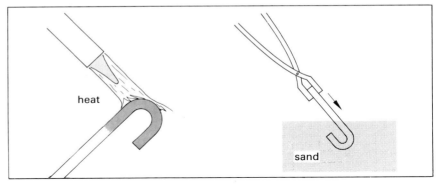

heat

sand

Fig. 2.24

Non-ferrous metals

Aluminium – because of its low melting point (660°C), there is a danger of overheating. To overcome this, coat it in soap which will act as a guide to the temperature. Soap turns black when heated to 400°C and aluminium is annealed at 350°C. Can you see the reason for using the soap?

Copper – heat gently until dull red (500°C) and cool slowly in air; or quench in water – the effect is the same. Overheating will cause black scaling on the surface of the copper, making it difficult to clean.

Brass – like copper, heat to a dull red and allow to cool slowly. If quenched in water, the metal is liable to fracture.

How should the hot metal be handled?

> Both copper and brass form a light oxide scale on their surfaces when heated. To remove this, place the cooled metal in a bath of dilute sulphuric acid. This is called **pickling**. Safety precautions have to be taken when doing this as the acid may splash.

Normalising

This is a very similar operation to annealing. It is used after steel has been worked cold. Heat the steel to cherry red (725°C) and then allow to cool in air. The cooling rate is fast, so small fine grains form, giving a much harder and tougher metal.

Hardening

It is possible to change some steels into very hard metals, capable of cutting itself in the soft state and other metals such as copper, brass and aluminium. To understand this, look at the structure of steel.

Structure of steel

Steel is made up of two elements: iron (Fe) and carbon (C). They appear in the metal in the following forms:

Ferrite – pure crystals of iron, which are soft and easily stretched;
Cementite – a chemical combination by weight of 1 of carbon to 14 of iron, normally called *iron carbide* (very hard and brittle);
Pearlite – alternate layers of ferrite and cementite (a very strong metal).

In making steel, carbon is added to iron (ferrite). These start to combine chemically, forming cementite. We now have layers of ferrite and cementite, making pearlite. As the carbon content is increased, more and more cementite forms; so the amount of pearlite increases. This continues until the point when the steel contains 0.83% carbon, and the structure is made up entirely of pearlite. If more carbon is added, some cementite begins to be left over from layers forming pearlite. We can show how these elements affect the properties of steel in a diagram.

Which heat treatment would we have to use on a piece of copper, while bending into our watch stand shape?

What does the diagram in Fig. 2.25 tell you about the ductility of steel?

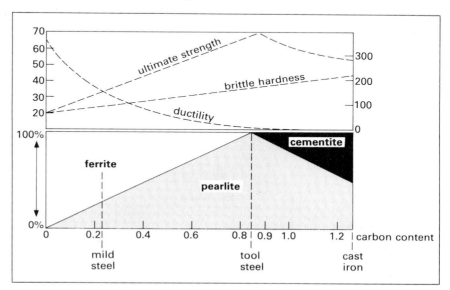

Fig. 2.25

The top half of the diagram shows how the properties of steel change as the carbon is added; the bottom half shows how the structure changes as the carbon content rises. As you can see, mild steel contains a large amount of iron (ferrite) and very little pearlite. This makes it soft and workable. Cast iron has much more cementite than pearlite, making it much harder and more brittle. When steel is made up entirely of pearlite, you obtain the maximum strength with good hardness. It is from this range of steels that we make cutting tools. The steel does, however, need a further change before this is possible.

What happens when the steel is heated

If we heat a piece of steel at a steady rate, and check it at intervals, the temperature will rise evenly to 720°C. It seems to remain at this temperature for a time before starting to rise again. It rises to 800°C at a much slower rate. Any further heating will see a return to the initial rate of temperature rise.

If the metal is allowed to cool, the reverse happens: the cooling slows down at the point at which it stopped when being heated. What is happening? The steel structure remains stable until it reaches 720°C; then the carbon within the layers of pearlite begins to dissolve into the iron. This is due to the iron structure changing from a body centred cubic to a face centred cubic. Once the change is complete, the temperature rises again. The carbon atom has now taken its place within the iron structure. At 910°C, the whole structure of the pearlite metal consists of a solid solution of carbon in iron. This is called **austenite**.

On cooling, the reverse takes place: the carbon reverts back. The temperature points at which the change of structure starts are known as the **critical points**. All steels have the same lower critical point (720°C), but the amount of carbon determines the upper critical point.

The chart in Fig. 2.26 shows that when steel is made up entirely of pearlite, the change is almost instant. This starts at 720°C and is completed by 730°C.

What colour do you think the metal will be at a temperature of 720°C?

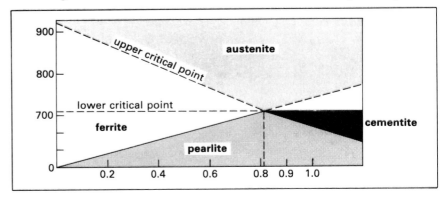

Fig. 2.26

Why do you think mild steel cannot become much harder by this method?

If the steel is dipped or quenched in water, the effect is quite startling. The soft steel becomes very hard and brittle. The iron structure has changed back to the body centred cubic, before the carbon has had time to escape. The result is a very distorted structure, which locks together forming an intensely hard metal. In this frozen state, the metal is called **martensite**. The quenching also has the effect of lowering the critical temperature at which pearlite changes to austenite, from 720°C to 300°C.

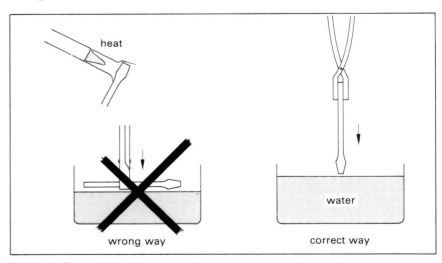

Fig. 2.27 Quenching

In this state, the metal is very hard, capable of resisting wear and of cutting other metals. It is also very brittle. Different degrees of hardness can be obtained by cooling in salt water (very hard), water (hard) and oil (quite hard).

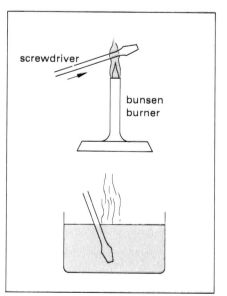

Fig. 2.28 Tempering

From Table 4 which tools will be very brittle?

Tempering

Steel in the martensite state is liable to chip or break when used as a tool. To overcome this, the metal can be gently reheated. This allows a small amount of carbon to escape from the iron structure which takes away some of the hardness and makes the steel tougher. In the workshop this is done by first cleaning the hardened steel with emery cloth, so that the oxide colours can be seen. Heat the metal in a gentle flame from a bunsen burner. Keep the heat a little distance from the part to be tempered. Oxide colours will start to form on the steel. Each oxide colour supplies a hint as to the temperature. This gives a guide to the amount of hardness.

Colour	Temperature guide	Possible uses
pale straw	230°C	lathe turning tools
dark straw	240°C	drills, milling machine cutters
brown	250°C	taps & dies, shear blades
brownish-purple	260°C	punches, planes, woodworkers' tools, reamers
purple	270°C	axes, press tools
dark purple	280°C	cold chisels, screwdriver blades
blue	300°C	saws, springs

Table 4

When the required colour nearly reaches the end, the steel must be quenched again in water. This stops any further change taking place. Industry uses ovens which can control the tempering to an exact degree; thus the metal does not need quenching.

Case hardening

It was stated earlier that mild steel remained quite soft and workable after heat treatment. Some degree of hardness can be given to mild steel if extra carbon is added to the outer surface. This is done in one of two ways:
1. The metal is first heated to cherry red and is then placed into carbon powder. When removed from the powder it is reheated to cherry red, before being quenched in water. This has the effect of changing the iron structure. With the extra carbon, it is able to form a larger amount of austenite than before. When quenched, this becomes martensite. The outer surface is now quite hard, and if the process is repeated the degree of hardness can be increased.

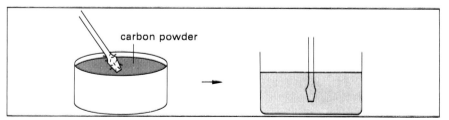

Fig. 2.29

How does a piece of case-hardened mild steel differ from a a piece of hardened tool steel?

2. The mild steel is placed in a metal box surrounded with charcoal granules (Fig. 2.30). The metal box is heated in an oven to 900°C, for several hours. Once again the outer skin becomes very hard with a soft inner core. With this method a degree of normal hardening and tempering can be done with the case-hardened mild steel.

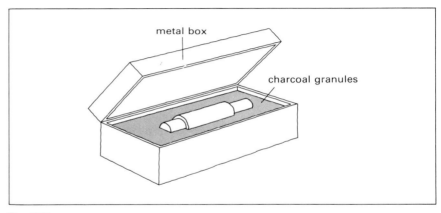

Fig. 2.30

Both methods will help mild steel to stand up to fairly heavy wear.

2.6 SHAPING METALS — CASTING

Why should the cast metal structure be stronger than the cut metal?

As metals can be turned into a liquid form if heated to a sufficiently high temperature, it is possible to use this state to make up complicated shapes. Make a mould or hollow copy of the shape in a suitable material e.g. sand. Pour into this the molten metal; on cooling, the required shape will form. This is called *casting*. It has major advantages over other shaping methods in that the shape is formed without wasting any material. The careful design of the mould can also help the metal to form into its strongest possible structure.

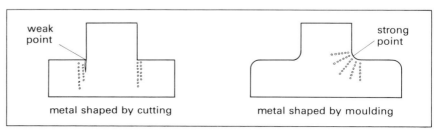

Fig. 2.31

Sand casting

This type of casting uses sand as the moulding material with clay added to help hold it together. Two types of sand are used: Mansfield or petrobond. *Mansfield or green bond* – has to be damped with water to make it hold together. It is termed as being green, because of its form not because of its colour. Once the mould is made in the sand, it has to be dried out, normally with a brazing torch. If it is not dried, when the molten metal is poured in a dangerous reaction takes place between the metal and water resulting in an explosion of metal. The main advantage of this system is that it is cheap and the sand can be re-used over and over again.

What problem will the wooden boxes have when used with Mansfield sand?

Why should metal patterns take so much longer to make than wood?

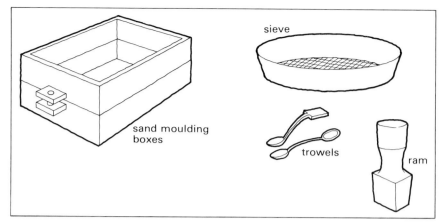

Fig. 2.32

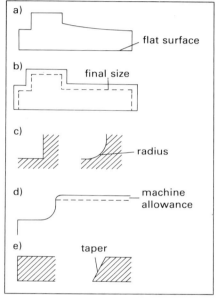

Fig. 2.33

Petrobond – a ready mixed sand, using oil as the binding agent. It is very safe to use as it contains no water, so drying out is not necessary. The major disadvantage is that it is relatively expensive and as the oil near the molten metal burns, this area of sand cannot be used again.

The sand is normally held in boxes or flasks made from wood, steel or cast iron. It will be the final design shape which will decide what size boxes are needed. A number of special tools are used for working the sand: a sieve to sift the sand, rammers to firm the sand down, trowels for touching up around the mould.

Before the moulding can start, a pattern of the final object has to be made. This is used to make the impression in the sand. When more than one casting is required, the pattern is normally made from wood. This is quite robust, but can easily be shaped. Metal patterns are used, but they take much longer to make up.

Once the pattern is made it can be used over and over again, but the sand mould has to be broken up in order to remove the cast metal shape.

The design of the pattern is of major importance if a successful casting is to be made. Certain points have to be included:
1. it should have one flat surface;
2. it should be slightly over size to allow for the molten metal shrinking during cooling (special over-size rulers are used by professional pattern makers);

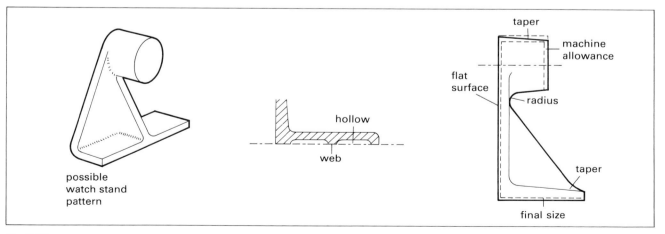

Fig. 2.34

Shaping metals

3. it should have all sharp internal corners rounded or radiused to avoid having weak points that may crack;

4. it should have an allowance for machining the surface, so that a smooth accurate finish is left where parts join;

5. it should have sides that taper or slope slightly (draft), to allow for the easy removal of the pattern from the sand;

6. it should have a good smooth surface finish, so that the impression will be a perfect copy of the design.

Sometimes the pattern is made with hollow areas to help reduce the weight of the final metal casting. To strengthen these areas, thin strips are placed across. These strips are called **webs**. The pattern needed to make our watch stand could look like Fig. 2.34.

If the final shape is to have no flat surface, the pattern is a little more complex. It has to be produced in two halves, one of which will have a flat surface. This is called a **split pattern**. It has locating pins to keep the two halves in line with moulding.

How does the web system help to reduce the final cost of the casting?

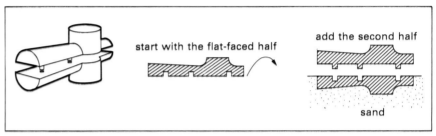

start with the flat-faced half

add the second half

sand

Fig. 2.35

Temporary patterns

If a single casting is required quickly, a one-off or lost pattern can be cut out of expanded polystyrene. This can be done with a heated tool or a hot wire cutter, as shown in Figs 3.54 and 3.55 on pages 138 and 139. As the pattern will remain in the sand, no draft is needed. The base should be used as the entry point for the molten metal so that it does not show on the final work. The molten metal vaporises the polystyrene as they touch, resulting in a burst of flames and heavy noxious fumes. As the pattern material contains air spaces a textured finish results. While this is of little use for engineering type work, it is ideal for more artistic design work.

How can the vaporising polystyrene be dangerous?

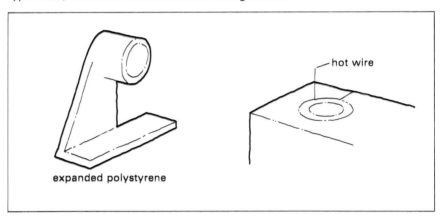

expanded polystyrene

hot wire

Fig. 2.36

2 Metals

How a sand mould is made up

The moulding boxes are chosen for the size of pattern. They are normally about 30mm larger all round. The boxes should be a matching pair, with pins or pegs for locating together.

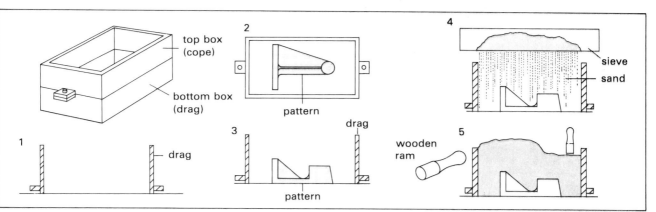

Fig. 2.37a)

Why should the pattern be kept away from the edges?

1. The bottom box or *drag* is turned upside down on a flat surface.
2. The pattern is placed inside in a central position.
3. The pattern is dusted with a parting powder, to stop the moulding sand from sticking to the pattern or the flat surface.
4. Sift moulding sand over the pattern until it is covered. Gently firm this into place around the pattern with your fingers.
5. Unsifted sand is added to the drag and rammed into place with a wooden ram until full.

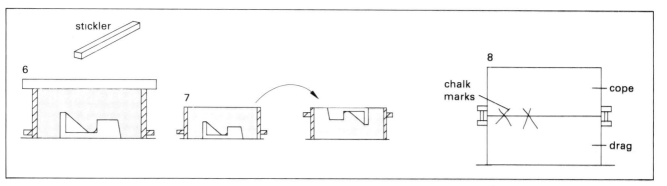

Fig. 2.37b)

6. The sand is levelled off or strickled with a straight edge.
7. The drag is then carefully turned over, the correct way up.
8. The top box or *cope* is fitted to the drag. Chalk marks are made on the box sides. This is to avoid mistakes when the boxes are parted for removing the pattern and then rejoined. (It is at this stage that a split pattern would have the second half joined.)

Shaping metals

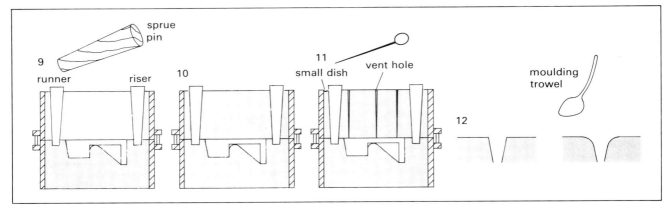

Fig. 2.37 c)

Why should the pegs be tapered?

Why do you think vent holes are needed?

9. Wooden tapered pegs (sprue pins) are placed at each end of the pattern. When these are withdrawn they will provide holes for a) getting their molten metal into the mould (**runner**) and b) allowing the air and gases to escape (**riser**).

10. Once again the surface is dusted with parting powder and sand is sieved over the pattern. Being a flat surface, only a small amount of sand is needed. The rest of the cope filled up with unsifted sand, rammed into place and strickled off.

11. Fine vent holes are made in the sand above the pattern. A small basin is cut in the sand near the runner pin, to help when pouring the molten metal. The two sprue pins are tapped lightly to loosen them. They are then carefully removed from the sand.

12. The sharp corners are trimmed round with a moulding trowel.

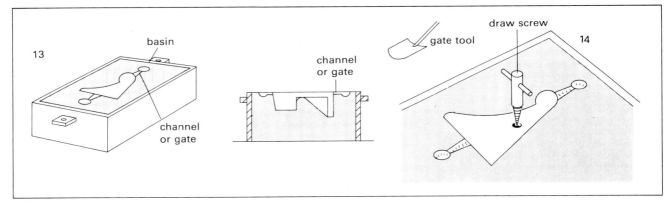

Fig. 2.37 d)

What danger do you think could be caused if the pouring is done while the boxes are standing on a concrete floor?

13. The two boxes are parted, and the cope is placed on one side. The drag has a basin cut at the base positions of the runner and riser. Small channels or gates are dug upwards from the basins to the pattern.

14. A draw screw is secured into the pattern and tapped gently. Once loose, the pattern is carefully lifted clear. All sharp edges in the basin or channel are smoothed out. Before the two boxes are rejoined, a pair of bellows is used to blow out any loose particles of sand. (It is at this point that green sand would need to be dried out.) The joined boxes are placed on a bed of sand. A weight should be placed across the top to stop any lifting taking place when pouring in the molten metal.

The metal to be used for the casting is heated in a special furnace. The steel industry uses a *cupola* (see page 53); while for school work, a crucible is used. The crucible furnace is heated by gas, and the metal is placed in a crucible made of plumbago. The normal metals used are shown in Table 4.

Metals	Pouring temperature	Uses
Aluminium alloys		
LM 4 aluminium + 5% silicon + 3% copper	680°C	general purpose casting
LM 6 aluminium + 12% silicon	720°C	for thin section casting
Zinc alloys		
KAYEM traces of lead, tin and cadmium	440°C	used for press tools
Copper alloys		
Brass English Standard: 65% copper + 35% zinc	1100°C	general purpose work with a decorative finish
Bronze Gunmetal: 90% copper + 10% tin	1200°C	instrument parts, valves, bearings

Table 5

 Extreme care is needed when handling molten metal. That is why it is the teacher or an experienced craftsperson who always does the pouring. Protective clothing should be worn in case of spillage. The metal is poured in a slow, steady manner, to allow a good even flux of metal through the mould.

What design advantage has this method over a drilled hole in a casting?

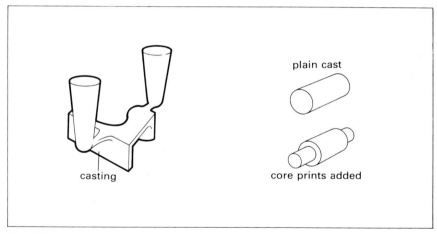

plain cast

casting

core prints added

Fig. 2.38

A flux is always added to the molten steel. Can you think why?

The mould is left until the metal has solidified and cooled. It is then removed from the sand and is **fettled**. This is the cutting off of the runner and riser, basin and gate, which are attached to the casting.

It is possible to make holes in a casting if it is designed into the pattern. Extra pieces are added to the pattern where the hole is required. These are called **core prints**. When set in the sand these will make extra spaces. A core or cylinder is now made up from baked sand. This is placed in position when the two boxes are pulled apart, and left in when they are replaced. The metal is poured in as before. On cooling, the mould is removed and the sand is knocked out, leaving a hole.

Shaping metals

Other forms of casting

Die casting

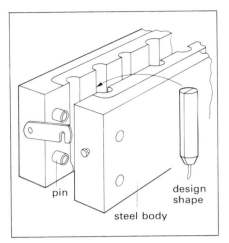

Fig. 2.39   Die casting

This type of casting uses metal moulds or dies, which have the design or shape cut into the surface. The moulds are normally made in two halves with pins that keep them in line and also form a clamping device. Considerable skill and time are needed to make up this type of mould. For mass production they are ideal, because they can be used over and over again, giving a very accurate and quick casting. Industry uses this form of casting a great deal. It can be seen in things made from zinc alloys, like toys, handles etc.

As the mould is metal it has to be pre-heated before use. This is to remove surface moisture and to prevent the casting metal from cooling or chilling too quickly on contact.

> What toys would you expect to see die cast?

> Why do you think the metal is melted in a charcoal block and not in a furnace?

Cuttlefish casting

With very small individual pieces of work such as jewellery, and using precious metals such as silver and gold, a cuttlefish bone is used as the mould. The bone is cut in half and the two cut surfaces are flattened by rubbing on a sheet of glasspaper or emery cloth.

Locating pegs are pushed through both pieces to keep the mould in line. The inside faces are now cut out to the design or pattern, or a model is placed between and the two halves are pressed together. The model system leaves an impression in both faces. Vent holes are made from the mould, and a large pouring hole is scratched out.

Then the cuttlefish is wired to a charcoal block that has a hollow in the top. Scrap pieces of casting metal are melted in the small hollow. The unit is tilted quickly to pour the molten metal into the mould.

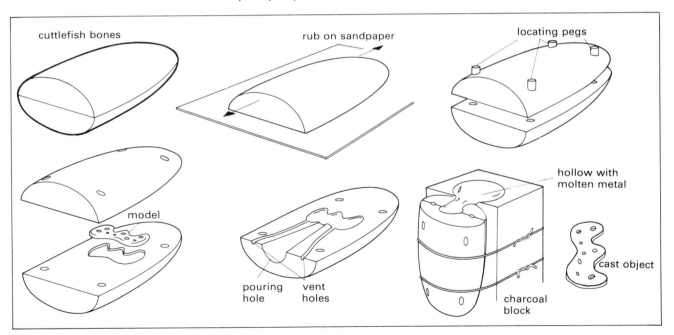

Fig. 2.40   Cuttlefish casting

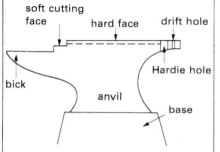

Fig. 2.41

What type of work can you think of that is made by forging?

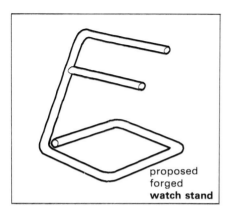

Fig. 2.43

2.7 SHAPING METALS – FORGING, BEATING, CUTTING AND MACHINING

Beating

Metals can be shaped with a hammer, if they are malleable. This can be done in the workshop in two ways: a) *hot working*; b) *cold working*.

Hot working

This is normally called **forging**, and is the age-old blacksmiths' art of shaping metals while they are in a red hot state. The metals that are used are mild steel, wrought iron and tool steel. When these metals are red hot they are very malleable. In schools, the traditional methods of heating metal are used: the blacksmiths' forge with coke and compressed air are the means of providing the hot fire. The metal is placed in the fire until it is glowing red; if left, it will burn (like a sparkler).

The metal is removed from the fire with tongs. It is ready for shaping on the anvil, using tools such as forging hammers, sets, fullers and swages. One of the early designs for the watch stand could well have been made in this way.

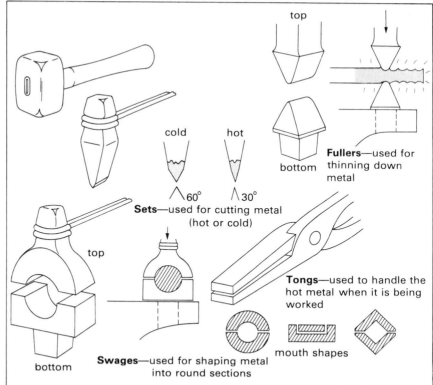

Fig. 2.42

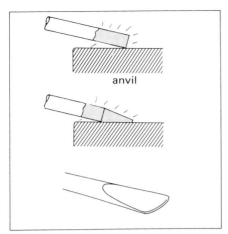

Fig. 2.44   Spreading

Forging processes

Some of the simple forging processes are as follows:

Spreading – as the hot metal is hit with the hammer it starts to flatten and spread out.

Drawing down to a taper (Fig. 2.45) – the metal is turned 90° before it is hit each time. This makes the metal into a square tapered shape. If a round taper is required, it is reheated and rotated as it is hit.

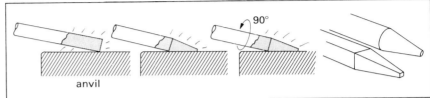

Fig. 2.45   Drawing down

What tools are made using the spreading method?

Why will the metal need reheating before it can be changed into a round taper?

Drawing down parallel (Fig. 2.46) the hot metal is hammered between fullers. This thins down the metal, if it is kept from spreading.

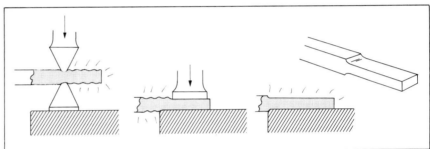

Fig. 2.46   Drawing down parallel

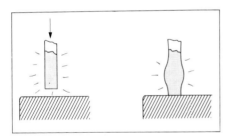

Fig. 2.47   Upsetting

Upsetting (Fig. 2.47) – this is done to increase the thickness of a piece of metal. The hot metal is banged down onto a hard surface (e.g. an anvil).

Twisting (Fig. 2.48) – as the metal is so soft, it is possible to twist it with a bar tool. This forms decorative metalwork.

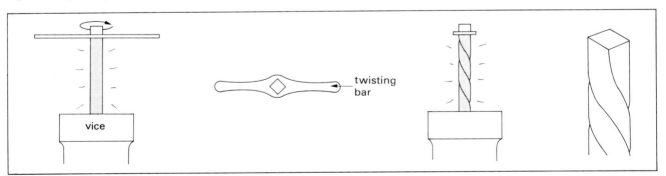

Fig. 2.48   Twisting

Punching and drifting (Fig. 2.49) – holes of many different shapes can be made in the hot metal, by punching them with a punch or drift.

What advantage has punching over a drilled hole?

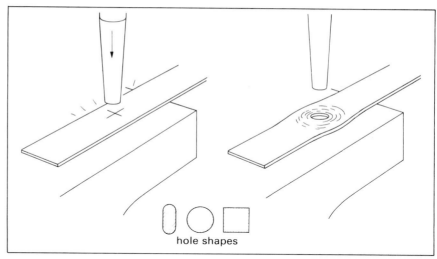

hole shapes

Fig. 2.49   Punching

Bending (Fig. 2.50) – is quite easy when the metal is hot. Corners can be formed by hitting the hot metal over the back of an anvil.

Forming rings (Fig. 2.51) – by using a bending former, it is possible to bend the metal round a number of times. If it is cut where it overlaps, rings can be formed.

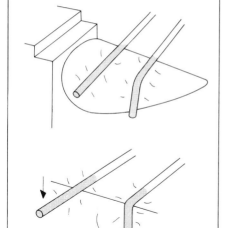

Fig. 2.50   Bending

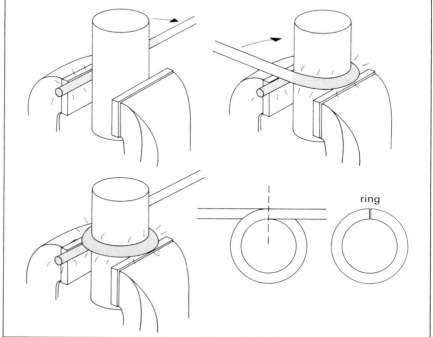

ring

Fig. 2.51   Ring forming

Shaping metals

81

Forming an eye (Fig. 2.52) – the bick of an anvil is used to form a number of bends and an eye can be formed as shown in Fig. 2.52.

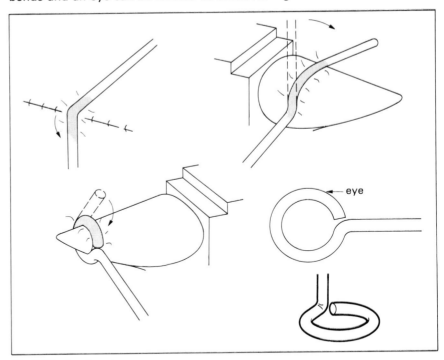

Fig. 2.52   Eye forming

Once all the work is complete, the hot metal should be quenched in water to cool it quickly. Some work may need quenching as it is being formed to stop further bending.

Cold working

Can you explain why some metals will crack if they are worked cold?

This method of shaping is only suitable for sheet metals, and can be done in two ways:
1. by folding, bending or rolling. This is called *sheet metalwork*.
2. by beating or hammering the metal to shape. This is called *beaten metalwork*.

Sheet metalwork

Sheet material	Description	Uses
Tinplate	Mild steel sheet with thin protective coating of tin	Food containers, boxes, trays, etc.
Terneplate	Mild steel sheet with thin coating of lead and tin	Less expensive than tinplate, but cannot be used for food containers
Galvanised sheet	Mild steel with thin coating of zinc	Weather protection surface material

Why should terneplate be of little use as food containers?

Plus sheet steel, aluminium, copper, brass, and gilding metal

Table 6

2   Metals

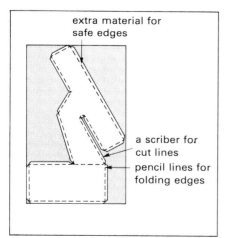

Fig. 2.53 Developed shape

extra material for safe edges

a scriber for cut lines

pencil lines for folding edges

All these materials have to be handled with care so that the protective coating is not damaged in any way. The work is normally marked out with a pencil to avoid scratching the surface, or it can be worked out full size on paper. This is then stuck to the metal surface with paste. As the work is to be bent or folded, the whole object has to be drawn in a developed or unfolded way. Lines or edges that need to be cut can be marked with a scriber, before being sheared with tinsnips. Extra material may need to be added for joints, and for making the metal edges safe.

The forming is done with a mallet, while the work is held in folding bars or around stakes. Some hammers are used just to tuck in joint edges.

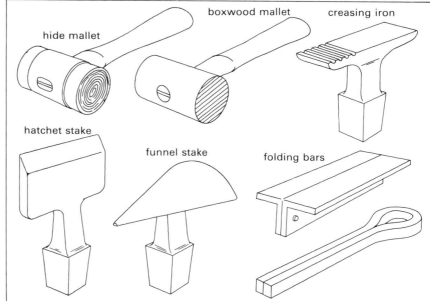

hide mallet

boxwood mallet

creasing iron

hatchet stake

funnel stake

folding bars

Fig. 2.54

As the bending is being done, any edges that are left exposed will be dangerous. Any such edge is bent over or folded to make it safe. This also stiffens up the side (Fig. 2.55).

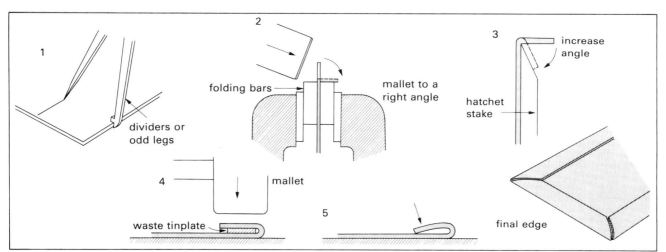

1

dividers or odd legs

2

folding bars

mallet to a right angle

3

increase angle

hatchet stake

4

waste tinplate

mallet

5

final edge

Fig. 2.55

For a stronger edge, the metal is folded over a piece of wire, which remains in place inside the edge. The allowance for the wired edge is 2½ times the thickness of the wire.

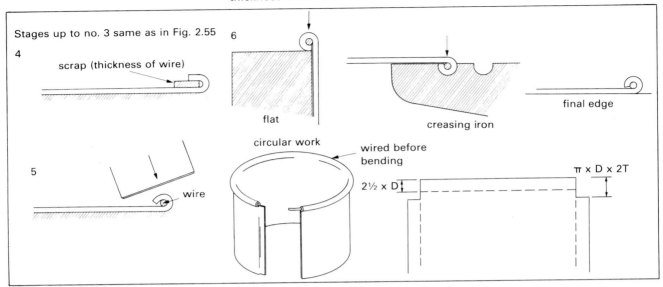

Fig. 2.56

If the sheet metal needs to be joined, a simple lap joint can be used. It is then soft soldered. Stronger joints can be made by folding the two joining edges so that they interlock (see Fig. 2.57).

Why are the different sheet materials not silver soldered or brazed?

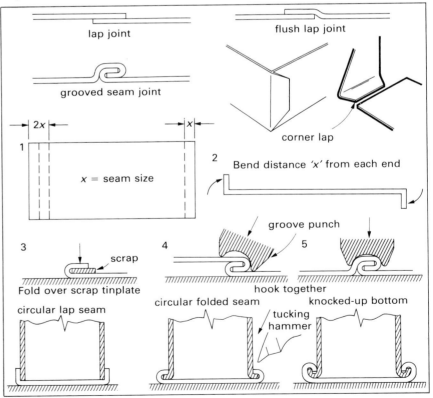

Fig. 2.57 Tinplate edges

Beaten metalwork

This is used to shape the decorative metals such as gold, silver, copper and brass sheet. The metals are hammered cold, but have to be annealed from time to time, as they will work harden. The metals are worked by special hammers or mallets on blocks and stakes.

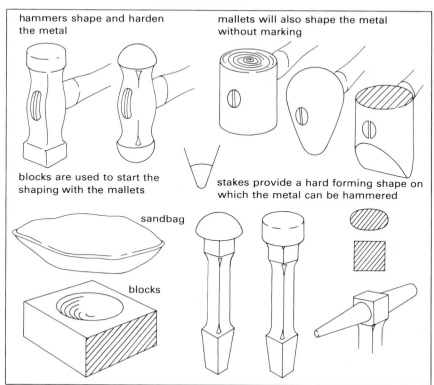

Fig. 2.58   Beating metalwork

With these simple tools the metal can be hollowed, dished, raised or turned from a flat sheet into a cylinder with a base.

In hollowing (Fig. 2.60), a blank sheet of metal is first cut to size, allowing extra metal for the curved shape. It is annealed, using an acid bath (see page 67) and then cleaned with pumice powder. A wooden block is cut out to the hollow shape, or a sandbag is used. The metal is placed on top and is malleted into the shape.

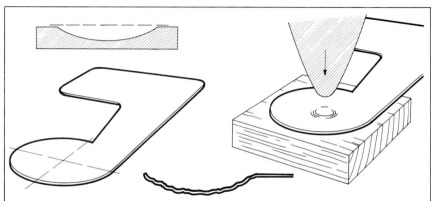

Fig. 2.60   Hollowing

Why do you think the metal needs to be cleaned after annealing?

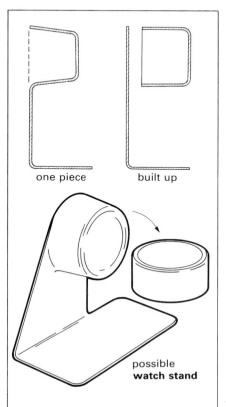

Fig. 2.59

In sinking, which is similar to hollowing, only part of the blank is shaped. This leaves a flat rim round the edge.

Planishing (Fig. 2.61) takes place after hollowing or sinking the metal. There will not be a true curve and the metal may still be soft in places. The surface can be trued up and hardened by using a planishing hammer over the metal.

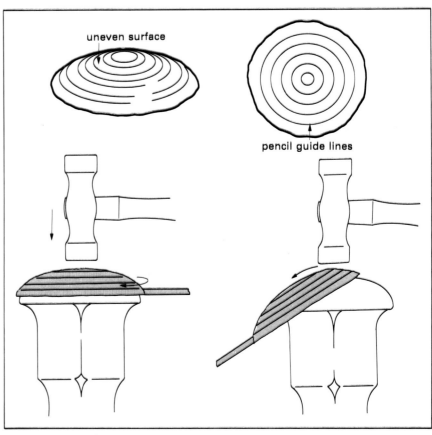

uneven surface

pencil guide lines

Fig. 2.61 Planishing

Examples of work

The dish is first marked with pencil circles, to act as guides for the hammering. Gently hammering from the centre outwards, the dish is slowly revolved. Following the circles round, the dish is tilted so that all the hammering is done at the centre of the stake.

When deeper containers are to be made, the method used is **raising** (Fig. 2.62). The work is first hollowed, then marked with the pencil circles. It is placed against a raising stake and hammered down. This starts to compress the metal and force it inwards. The shape begins to form. After each complete round of hammering, the metal has to be annealed and cleaned. The process is repeated many times before the final shape is completed. This method takes a long time and should be compared with the building up of work by joining or seaming.

The raised shape has to be planished again to true up the surface.

As planishing tends to thin the metal, the edge of the container may need thickening. This is completed by hammering or **caulking**, or by soldering on a ring to create a fat lip. Once the raised shape is complete the height can be trued up. It is then cut to size with universal snips, before being rubbed on an emery board to finish.

What is the advantage of the
raised method if it takes so long?

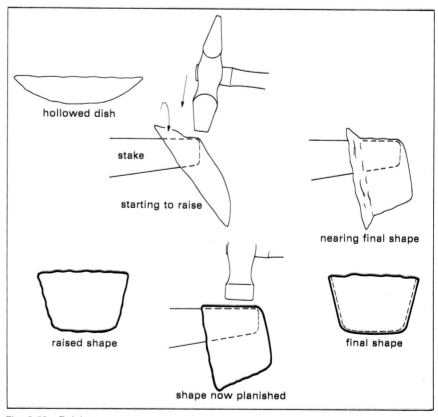

Fig. 2.62   Raising

Simple shapes can be made by joining beaten work together. This saves a great deal of time and energy. The work can be folded to shape if it is first given a vee groove. In this way square, hexagonal or rectangular shapes can be made, with the last joint or seam silver soldered. Cylindrical and conical shapes can be rolled to shape before joining the butt seam. The work will involve holding the work together by wire, split pins or a weight, while the joining takes place. The work depends on the joining being well done. It can allow some further shaping to be done.

Why should the seam joint be as
fine as possible?

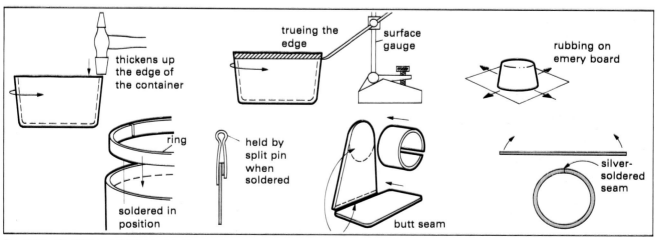

Fig. 2.63   Caulking and joining beaten work

Shaping metals

Cutting

This is perhaps the major method of shaping metal; and many alloys are developed with this in mind, for easy machinability. (Lead alloyed with steel gives a very free cutting steel.) Areas of the metal are cut away to form the required shape. It has the advantage of being able to use standard sizes of material that can be turned into complicated pieces. The disadvantage is that a large amount of material is wasted.

For any metal-cutting tool to work it must be hard and wedge shaped. This is due to the fact that metal is forced apart or torn. Only after this is the surface made smooth.

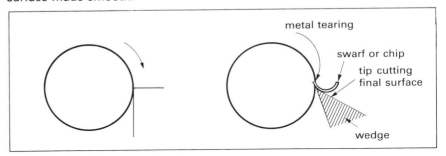

Fig. 2.64

The shape and size of the wedge will vary according to the metal being cut. All wedges, however, must have two things:
1. *rake* – which gives the tool its penetration and strength;
2. *clearance* – which gives the tool its clear working space so that only the tip is in contact.

These two factors (rake and clearance) apply to all metal-cutting tools, from the hand tool to machine tools, from hacksaw to drill.

What do you think would happen to the tool and the work if no clearance was given?

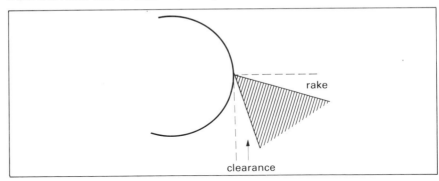

Fig. 2.65

Hand cutting tools

These are the tools that are hand held and so work at fairly slow speeds. The general ones are the file, hacksaw, cold chisel, taps and dies. All of these are made from high carbon steel (tool steel) which has been hardened and tempered.

The **file** is the foremost hand-held shaping tool. It is made in a wide range of shapes or cross-sections; each designed for filing certain shapes.

All files are cut in the same way, by having the blade grooved at an angle. This forms tiny wedges or teeth. Some files have a single groove, others have two which cross at different angles to give quicker cutting (see Fig. 2.66). Each tooth is given negative rake to make it as strong as possible.

How can chalk and a wire brush help to keep a file clean?

2 Metals

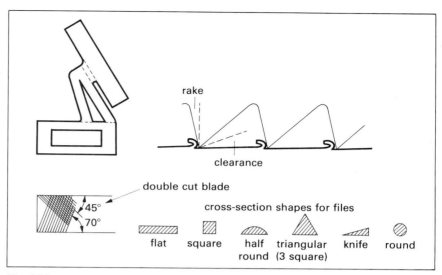

Fig. 2.66

Which files would you use to trim the watch stand to shape?

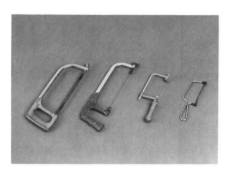

A **hacksaw** is a thin flexible blade stretched or tensioned between a frame. The size of frame varies from the large hacksaw to the smaller junior hacksaw, to the piercing saw. Each has its own size blade and method of tensioning. The blades, however, all have a similar type of teeth with very little rake – for maximum strength. The teeth are also bent or SET over at the tips to give clearance when cutting. This stops the work from binding on the blade sides.

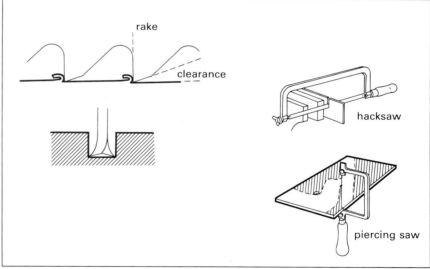

Fig. 2.67

Why does a thin blade need to be tensioned before it can be used?

The tension file (abra-file) is another frame tool which is a thin flexible steel wire cut like a file. By using special links it can be used in a hacksaw frame. It cuts in any direction and has a wide range of uses, including cutting intricate shapes.

Shaping metals

A **cold chisel** is normally a piece of hexagonal high carbon steel which cuts when struck with a hammer. The tip is sharpened or ground, depending on the metal to be cut: a sharp wedge for soft metal; thicker for harder metals. By holding the chisel at different angles and working on a 10° clearance, the correct rake is obtained.

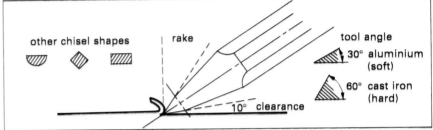

Fig. 2.68

What other workshop tool can you think of which has a shearing action?

Snips are cut in a different way to the other tools in that the tool has two blades. The blades are used to push the metal in different directions or to shear the metal in half. The blades have clearance, but no rake. They are used for cutting SHEET material. They can be straight, curved or universal pattern.

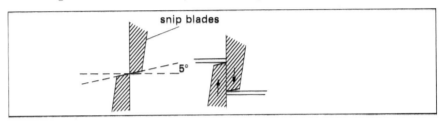

Fig. 2.69   Shear action

Machining

Machine cutting tools have to work at much faster speeds than hand tools. A different metal is therefore used because friction causes carbon steel to heat up quickly and so loses its hardness and temper. The alloy used is *high speed steel* (18% tungsten), which will cut at very high temperatures without any problems. By using machine tools, it is possible to produce work quickly and accurately, with an excellent finish.

The drilling machine

This holds the cutting tool by means of a chuck or tapered spindle, and revolves it at high speed. In the workshop we tend to use two main types: the small portable electric drill and the fixed pillar drill. The pillar drill, with its sensitive feed and fixed working table, is the more accurate of the two.

Fixed pillar drill

Why do you think small drills are parallel, while large drills are tapered?

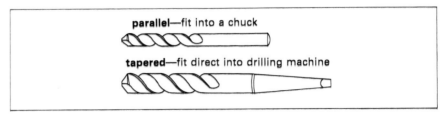

Fig. 2.70   Twist drills

The main cutting tool for the drilling machine is the twist drill. This is made in a wide range of sizes. The small sizes are parallel and fit into the chuck; while the larger drills, over 12mm diameter, are tapered to fit into the drilling machine spindle.

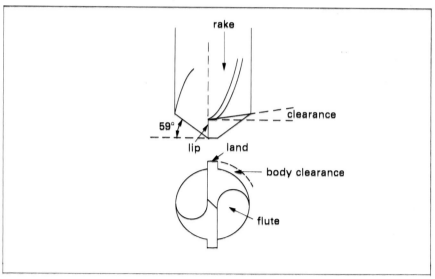

Fig. 2.71

The drill is sharpened, or ground, to give two equal cutting edges or lips. Each has clearance and the twist or flute gives the rake. If the lips are unequal, the drill will produce an over-size hole. The body of the drill is also given clearance but has two small lands that keep the drill true as it works.

Bad sharpening can affect the cutting action (see Fig. 2.72).

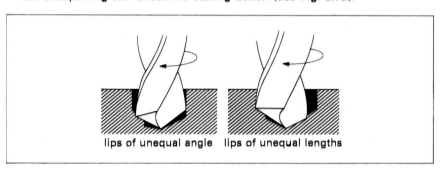

Fig. 2.72

Flat drill (top), centre drill (centre), countersunk drill (bottom)

How would you make up a flat drill from a piece of round tool steel?

Other drills

Flat drill – can be made up in the workshop from high carbon steel; useful for drilling flat sheet or a piece of hard material. It is not suitable for deep holes; it is not parallel, so it will not drill a true hole.

Countersunk drill – does not drill holes, but opens out ready drilled holes to an angle for screw or rivet heads. This allows them to fit flush with the surface.

Centre drill – used for positioning the centre of the work on the lathe. It is also used for starting the centre in a piece of round work.

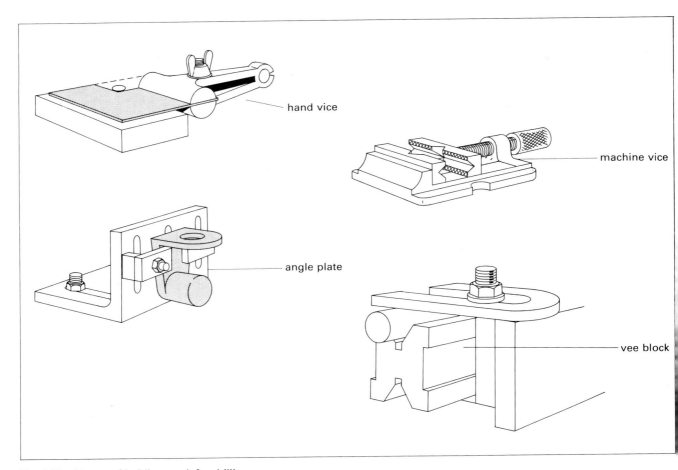

Fig. 2.73 Means of holding work for drilling

The centre lathe

This is perhaps the most important tool used in the metalworkshop, because it can perform so many different cutting operations. It can smooth a surface, reduce material in size, cut material to length, drill holes, bore large holes, and cut screw threads. The lathe works by holding the material and then rotating or turning it at speed, while a cutter is moved across, along or into the surface.

How does the drill action differ on a lathe from that on a drilling machine?

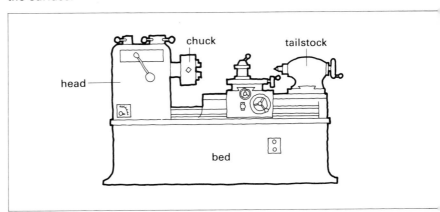

Fig. 2.74 Centre lathe

The work can be held on to the lathe in a number of ways. It is the size and shape of the blank material which must be used. Some methods are as follows:

Three-jaw self-centring chuck – used for holding circular or hexagonal work. It is quick to operate – by turning a single key. All work must be completed before removal from the chuck or inaccurate pieces will result. Two sets of jaws are available.

Four-jaw independent chuck – used for holding square, round or irregular shaped work. The work has to be set into a central position by using a testing instrument, such as a dial test indicator. Each jaw moves independently, is reversible and has very good holding power.

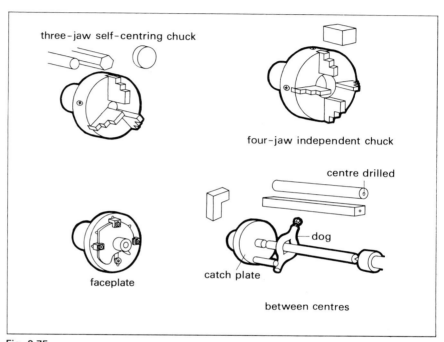

Fig. 2.75

Which method do you think could be used for our cast aluminium watch stand (Fig. 2.76)?

Faceplate – used when the work is difficult or impossible to hold by any other method. The work has to be clamped or bolted in position, with balance weights added to make it spin true.

Between centres – used for turning long pieces of work. The work is held between two centre supports. It is revolved by a carrier or dog which is clamped to it, and driven by a striking pin and plate. All work has to be centre drilled before it can be held.

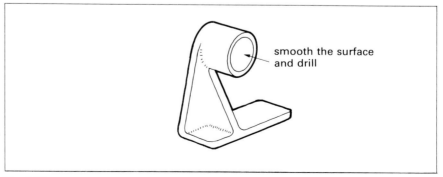

Fig. 2.76

Shaping metals

Tool forms

The cutting tool is normally fitted into a holder, which is then set up to a central position in a toolpost. If the tool is not set up correctly, poor work will result and the tool may break due to digging into the surface.

Four-way toolpost – can carry four different tools at one time, but needs scrap packing to lift the tool to a central position.

Pillar toolpost – less stable than the four-way type, but is easily adjusted by means of a rocker or boat. This adjustment does however alter the rake and clearance angles on the cutting tool.

The lathe tool is ground to provide the rake and clearance both at the front and the side; the amount depends on the metal which is being cut. It is a general rule that the harder the material the smaller the rake and clearance.

What advantages has the four-way toolpost over the pillar toolpost?

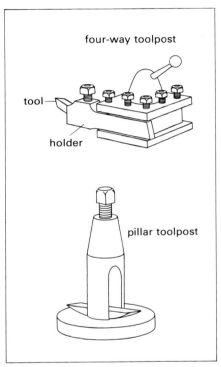

Fig. 2.77   Four-way toolpost
             Pillar toolpost

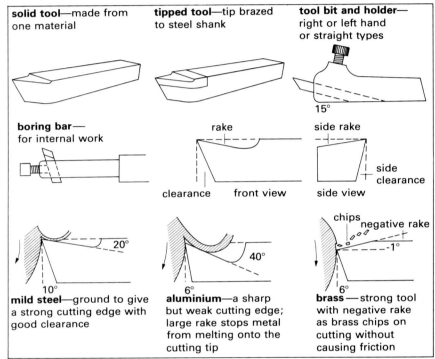

Fig. 2.78   Tool forms

Why do you think a lathe tool needs rake and clearance at both front and side?

The lathe tool is also ground to shape for different types of work: rough cutting, smooth finishing, parting off, screw cutting.

2 Metals

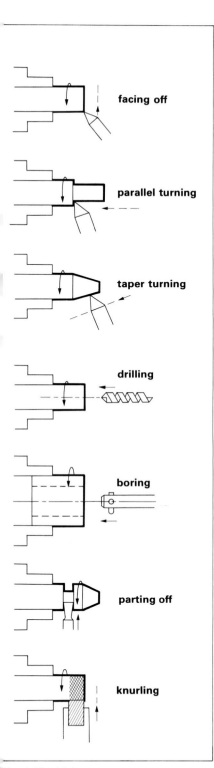

Processes

Some of the main processes that can be tackled on the lathe are as follows (Fig. 2.79):

Facing off

Normally the first operation; the tool is moved at right angles to the centre, trueing the end surface.

Parallel turning

The cutting tool is moved sideways or parallel to the centre, forming a cylinder. As more cuts are taken the work is reduced in diameter.

Taper turning

The tool is moved at an angle to the centre, producing a taper or cone shape. The taper can be formed in three main ways:
1. by using the tool angle for very small tapers or chamfers;
2. by setting the compound slide at the required angle and feeding the tool with the slide handle (medium size tapers are possible, due to the limit of the slide feed screw);
3. by setting over the tailstock, so that it is out of line with the headstock. The work is then angled to the direction of the carriage, so that it can cut as if for parallel turning (long tapers possible).

Drilling

The tailstock is used as the drill holder, either by fitting a chuck or by using the taper hole. The process starts by first fitting and using a centre drill to locate and start the hole accurately. This is replaced with the next correct size drill. This is fed slowly into the work with the tailstock control handle.

Boring

To increase the size of a hole a tool is fitted to a boring bar, which is moved inside parallel to the surface.

Parting off

When the work needs to be trimmed to length or parted from the extra material held in the chuck, a narrow tool is fed into the material. This not only parts the work but also faces the end.

Knurling

Makes it possible to provide a grip system on a metal surface by pressing into it a straight or diamond-shaped pattern. This is done by hardened steel knurling wheels held in an adjustable holder or head.

Fig. 2.79 Main processess

Why should parting off on the lathe be better than cutting to size with a hacksaw?

We can now look at how these processes are used for making a simple object e.g. a small foot for our watch stand.

Stage 1 – an aluminium block of ⌀15 is mounted in a three-jaw chuck, as shown in Fig. 2.80.

Stage 2 – the end of the material is faced off, using a round nose tool.

Stage 3 – centre drill and then drill the ⌀5 hole to the correct depth: 12mm.

Stage 4 – parallel turn down the ⌀10 section, to the correct diameter and length using a finishing tool. Check the size with a micrometer.

Stage 5 – the remaining ⌀10 is now knurled at a slower speed.

Stage 6 – the parting tool is now set up on the toolpost, and the work is parted from the chucking material.

Stage 7 – the knob is reversed in the chuck and held by the ⌀10, and the short taper is cut with the finishing tool set at an angle.

Why should the knob not be held by the knurled section, when it is reversed?

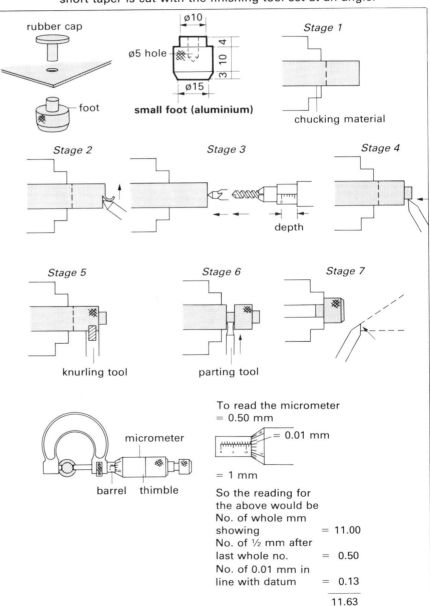

Fig. 2.80

When the cutting tool is moved backwards it is designed to lift. Can you think why?

Shaping machine

This is another important machine tool used in the workshop. It uses similar shaped cutting tools to the lathe. They are held in a vertical position and are pushed over the material surface to cut. The size of the cutting tool is quite large to give the extra strength required for the sudden shock load at the start of the cutting stroke. Each forward stroke cuts a fine groove; the work is moved sideways on the return stroke. It is an ideal tool for machining large flat areas very quickly. All work has to be clamped or bolted to the machine table.

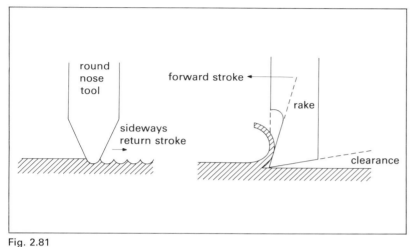

Fig. 2.81

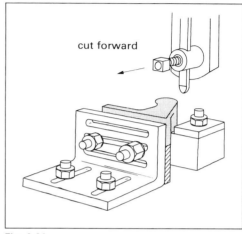

Fig. 2.82

Shaping machine

Milling machine

Milling machine

There are two main types of milling machine: those that hold a multi-point cutter in a vertical position and those that hold it in a horizontal position. Both systems, however, revolve the cutter at speed so that a continuous action

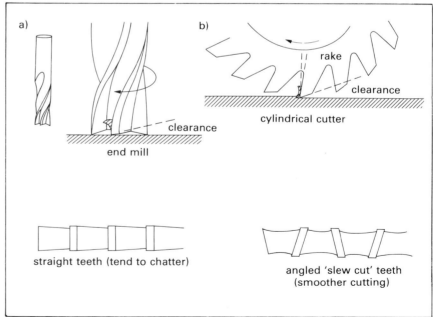

Fig. 2.83

takes place. A wide range of work is possible – from cutting flat surfaces to slots, grooves, rebates and even gear cutting. All work has to be clamped or bolted to a machine table.

1. cutters held in a vertical position are either **end mills** or **slot drills** – they use the twist or flute to provide the tool rake;

2. cutters held in a horizontal position range from large **cylindrical cutters** to narrow **side and face cutters**; some are angled, others are curved or formed. They can be used on their own or placed together in a gang for multi-cutting. The teeth are similar to those in a hacksaw. The best type have the teeth in a spiral form, to give a gradual cutting action and so reducing vibration.

When milling, the work should always be as rigid as possible.

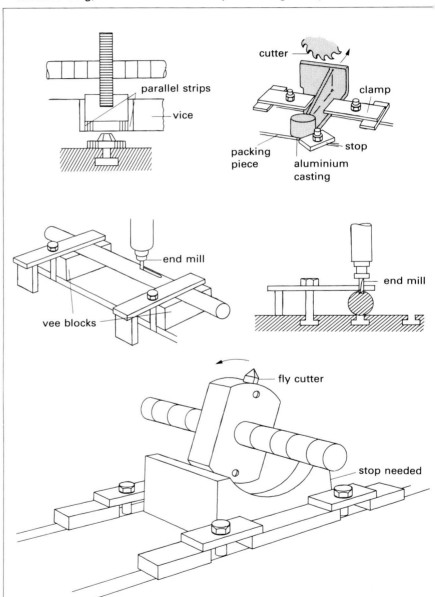

Fig. 2.85

When using a horizontal cutter it is always best to cut the material in an uphill direction as shown in Fig. 2.84, and not downhill. Can you suggest why?

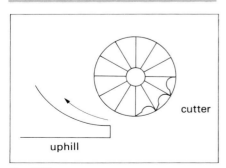

Fig. 2.84

2.8 JOINING METALS

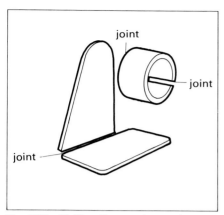

Fig. 2.86   Making the watch stand from pieces

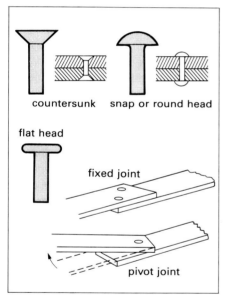

Fig. 2.87   Rivets

What rivet would be best for the rivet in Fig. 2.88?

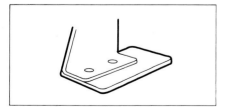

Fig. 2.88

As most design work will involve more than one piece of metal, some knowledge of joining metals is necessary. This could be joining to similar metals or to other materials. The joining of metals can be divided into two categories: (1) *cold joining*; (2) *hot joining*. Both of these methods have advantages and disadvantages and it must be the final use of the design work that decides which is to be used.

Cold joining

As the title suggests the metal is joined when cold so that no distortion is caused. The metal may, however, be weakened by having to drill holes with some of the methods.

Rivets

The rivet method is to drill holes into the work pieces and to use metal pegs or rivets, which form the joining system when hammered over. The joint is strong and permanent and can only be separated by drilling out the rivet.

Manufactured rivets – ready made in a wide range of sizes, materials and shaped heads. They are made from metals such as mild steel, aluminium, brass, copper – all in a ready annealed state for hammering. The common types are shown in Fig. 2.87.

Countersunk rivet – the most common; used when a level or flush surface needs to be left after joining.

Snap or round head rivet – used when maximum strength is needed and a flush surface does not matter or where countersinking would weaken the work.

Flat head rivet – used mainly for thin sheet material – to spread the joint.

Bifurcated rivet – used for joining other materials to metal e.g. leather and plastics.

Working out the size of rivet needed for a joint, is based upon the thickness of the pieces to be joined. The general rule is that the length of the rivet should be the total thickness of the work plus (1) the diameter (D) of the rivet so that the countersunk head can be formed and (2) one and a half times the diameter (1½D) of the rivet so that the snaphead can be formed.

The forming of the rivet end is done by using a ball pein hammer. First

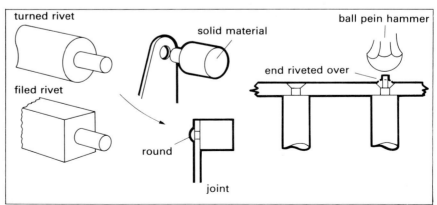

Fig. 2.89

What would you use to help a pop rivet hold down a material like leather?

support the head on a flat surface for a countersunk rivet or on a dished or dolly support for a snap rivet. For final shaping of the end use the flat face of the hammer for the countersunk and a set tool for the snap head.

It is possible at times to use the work itself as the peg or rivet, by filing or lathing it down. This acts as both a locating piece and a joining method.

A **pop rivet** is a special type of rivet which is hollow and is used when it is impossible to hammer or hold the ends of a normal rivet. A special pulling tool has to be used to withdraw the forming pin. The shape for joining can then be formed. Pop rivets have only limited strength, but are ideal for joining light metals (see Fig. 2.90).

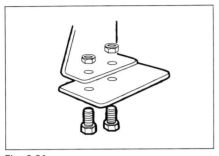

Fig. 2.91

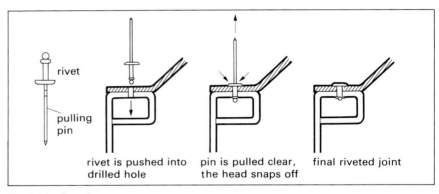

rivet is pushed into drilled hole   pin is pulled clear, the head snaps off   final riveted joint

Fig. 2.90   Pop rivet

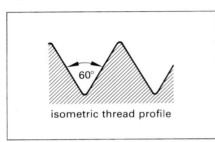

isometric thread profile

Fig. 2.92

Screws

This method of joining again involves drilling holes into the work, but this time it provides for a system of assembly and disassembly. It uses a form of screw thread or helical groove, which may be vee shapes, square etc. The type, size and strength of the joint will determine the size and thread form of the screw to be used.

Manufactured screws come in agreed standard sizes, with a range of head shaped, turning methods and materials. All of them use the vee form thread.

The one in general use is the International Standards Organisation (ISO) METRIC, ranging from 1mm to 100mm in size. Older type vee threads may be found in use: British Standard Whitwirth (BSW), British Association (BA) and many others. The common types are shown in Table 7.

Type of screw	Description	Uses
Bolt	Hexagonal or square head; small proportion of length is threaded	Use with nut and washer
Set screw	Similar to bolt, but no nut; usually threaded whole length	Used for screwing directly into piece of work
Machine screw	Much smaller – range of head shapes; turned by screwdriver	Used for holding small parts together accurately
Grub screw	Very small, no head; turned by screwdriver or hexagonal wrench	Used to lock parts in place
Coach bolt	Curved head and square on shank	Used for holding wood to metal
Stud	Simple rod, threaded at both ends	Screws into work and acts as locating piece for another part
Self-tapping screw	Cuts its own thread	Used for joining thin metals

Table 7

hexagonal nut   plain washer

wing nut   spring washer

caste nut   serrated washer

nylon insert

ny-lock   tab washer

Fig. 2.93

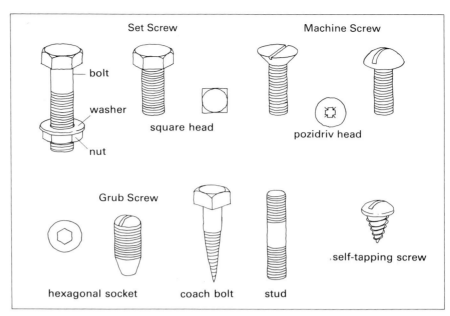

Why do you think washers are used with bolts?

There is a range of manufactured nuts and washers. These are designed for special purposes, e.g. locking devices, shakeproof devices etc.

Workshop made screws are employed when it is possible to use the work itself as the screw system or part of the screw system. Special tools are used to cut the threads:
1. *die* – a hardened circular split nut;
2. *set of taps* – hardened screws.
    The **die** is held in a special holder which has adjusting screws. If tightened, these screws will make the die close slightly so that it will cut smaller. The die is used to thread smaller rods by turning it back and forth, until a thread is formed (Fig. 2.94).

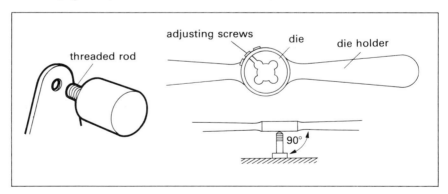

Fig. 2.94

Why do you think the die is adjustable and the tap not?

The **taps** are made in sets of three: taper, second and plug. Each is held in turn for cutting the thread inside a hole. Each thread size has a recommended hole that must be drilled, before tapping can start. As the hole is smaller than the final thread, the tapered tap is used first to start off the thread form. This is followed by the second tap which is more parallel. The thread is completed by the plug tap which is the exact size and shape. Each tap is held in a special holder or wrench, and turned back and forth. A lubricant, normally oil, is used to help the cutting action.

Joining metals   101

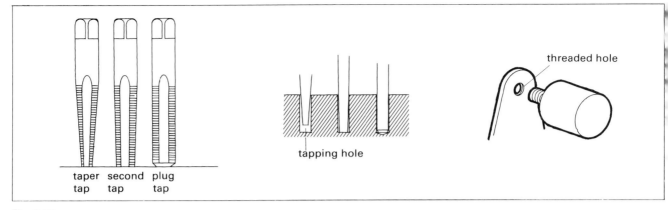

Fig. 2.95

By using the taps and dies, it is possible to design and make up many different forms of nuts and bolts, locking devices, handles, knobs and screws. Each has a particular purpose, such as hand-controlled nut or lever.

Why should a vee thread be weaker than a square thread of similar size?

Special **machine made screws** are used in place of the weaker vee thread when screws have to withstand or apply very heavy pressure. These special thread forms can only be cut on an engineers' lathe or on special screw machines, with a cutter sharpened or ground to the thread form. In this way, only the size of the machine limits the size of the thread.

Square thread screws are very powerful, but do not engage well, if the threads have to come together. They are used on such things as clamps, vices etc. Buttress thread screws have power in one direction only, but can be used for quick release. They are found on such things as a woodworkers' vice. Acme thread screws are used in place of the square thread when screws have to engage e.g. lathe lead screw.

Hot joining

With this system of joining some form of heating is required to help form the joint. How much heat depends on how strong the joint needs to be and if the work can stand this without melting. The methods vary from very little heat

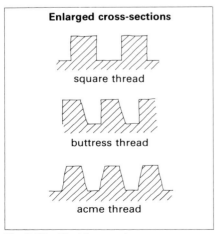

Enlarged cross-sections

square thread

buttress thread

acme thread

Fig. 2.96   Machine made screws

to the melting point of the metal. The range is shown in Table 8. Each method has an important part to play in the joining of metals, and in many cases a lower temperature joining system can follow a higher one. In this way, an earlier joint is not melted.

Method	Working temperature	Uses
Soft soldering	185°C to 250°C	For joints on light items – e.g. electrical, tinplate – and general work.
Silver soldering	620°C to 800°C	For low temperature work with reasonable strength e.g. brass, gilding metal.
Brazing	875°C to 900°C	For relatively strong joints that can withstand a reasonable amount of heat e.g. general steel work.
Welding	The melting point of the metal	The joint should be as strong as the work material.

Table 8

Why would zinc chloride be of little use for electrical work?

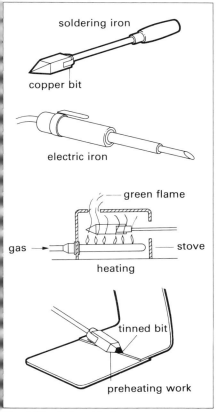

Fig. 2.97   Soft soldering

Soft soldering

This form of joining uses an alloy of lead and tin, known as soft solder. This melts and forms the joint. Different types are available, but the general one is made up of 50% lead and 50% tin. The work is first cleaned and then fluxed (with zinc chloride for steel and brass; with resin and tallow for copper and electrical connections). The flux acts as a surface cleaner during heating, preventing oxides and scale forming. This helps the soft solder to flow. It should be noted that an acid flux (e.g. zinc chloride) needs to be washed from the work after joining or it will continue to eat the metal away. Aluminium is difficult to soft solder, because its oxide skin forms so quickly. Special solders and fluxes have to be used.

When soft soldering, the heat is applied by using a heated iron, which is first cleaned then dipped into the flux. The tip of the iron is now tinned i.e. it has a small amount of solder melted on to it. The heated iron is drawn slowly backwards along the fluxed joint. As the iron moves it pre-heats the metal and the solder runs off the tip into the joint (Fig. 2.97).

Sometimes the work is difficult to solder with an iron, being too large to heat or too awkward to get at; so a method called **sweating** is used. With this method the work is cleaned, fluxed and heated on a stove. The two surfaces to be joined are then tinned or covered with solder. They are placed together and reheated or sweated. The solder remelts, flows together and the work is allowed to cool.

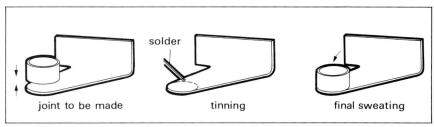

Fig. 2.98   Sweating

Soft soldering is a quick method of joining and is ideal for thin or small pieces of metal. It can also be used to hold larger pieces temporarily. It does, however, have limited strength.

How else could the metal be heated for sweating?

Silver soldering

This gives a much wider range of melting points than soft soldering combined with high strength. An alloy of silver, copper and zinc is used as the joining material. The amount of each gives the variation in temperatures (Table 9).

Grade	% silver	% copper	% zinc	% cadmium	Melting point	Flux
Easy flow	50	15	16	19	620°C	Easy-Flo
Medium	61	29	10	0	750°C	Tenacity
Hard	43	37	20	0	800°C	Tenacity

Table 9

The reason for the different grades is that work can be built up from a number of pieces added to each other. If one joint is to be melted while another joint is not, different alloys must be used in each. By varying the composition of the alloy, different temperatures can be used. For example, when making a tankard, the following method would be used:

after the metal surface has been cleaned, the joint is fluxed with **Borax** (*Easy Flo* for below 725°C, *Tenacity* for above). These are sold in a powder form, but applied as a paste. Mix the powder with water to make a thin paste and apply. It will stay in place during the heating. The work is then held together in some way e.g. using wire, split pins or a weight which will not melt or take heat from the joint. Small snippets of solder are placed at intervals along the joint line. The joint is gently heated with a brazing torch until the flux dries; then the heat is increased. At the correct temperature, the snippets melt and flash along the joint. The work is then allowed to cool before being cleaned in an acid bath.

Why do you think the work needs to be wired?

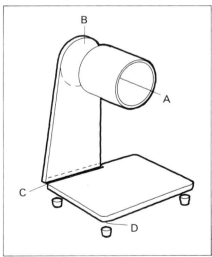

Fig. 2.100

If we made up our watch stand from copper as shown in Fig. 2.100, what grades of silver solder would you use for the joints?

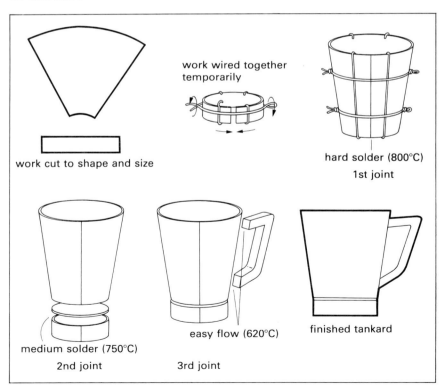

Fig. 2.99 Silver soldering

The metals that can be joined using silver solder are: steel, brass, copper, silver (*not* aluminium). The main disadvantage with this method is the high cost of the silver solder.

Brazing

If an extra piece of metal has to be joined to the work after all three grades had been used, how could it be fixed?

This is a high temperature joining method, using an alloy of copper and zinc which we call **spelter**. It gives a very tough, strong joint which is able to withstand great strain. As the temperature is so high it is mainly used for joining the ferrous metals. Two grades of spelter are made (see Table 10).

Spelter	% copper	% zinc	Melting point	Flux
Medium	54	46	885°C	Borax
Hard	60	40	900°C	Borax

Table 10

What would happen if the work was not fluxed first?

The work is fluxed with borax and held together by a peg joint, wire or a weight. It is heated with a brazing torch until the work is cherry red; the flame is removed and it is the heat of the work that now melts the spelter, as it is touched on the joint. The work is then allowed to cool.

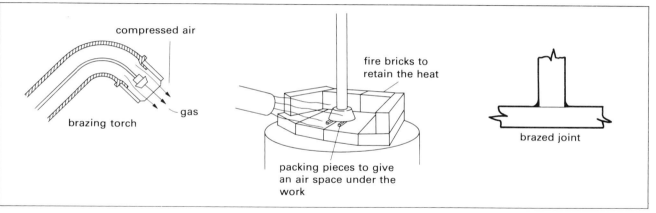

Fig. 2.101   Brazing

The main disadvantage is that by using the brazing torch a very large area of work has to be heated: some distortion or movement may take place and spoil the work.

Welding

This is the joining together of similar metals, using a welding or filler rod of the same material e.g. steel to steel, aluminium to aluminium. No flux is used when joining steels but special fluxes are used on other metals. This method involves melting the edges of the two joining metals, and adding the filler rod to form one material. The joint is very strong as it should be the same strength as the two materials; sometimes it tends to be a little brittle if put under strain. Due to the high melting point of some metals a very high temperature heat source is needed. This can be either: a) oxygen/acetylene gas welding; b) electric arc welding. Each of these gives intense heat over a small area. Oxygen/acetylene welding is the most common method in schools; the electric arc welding glare is dangerous unless it is confined to a booth or special room.

Goggles have to be worn with the oxygen/acetylene system.

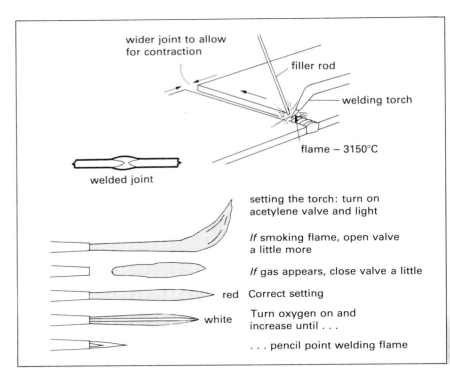

Fig. 2.102 Oxygen/acetylene welding

What advantage has welding over brazing for accurate work?

The blacksmith also has a method of welding. This involves heating the two pieces of metal to melting point in a forge, before hammering them together.

2.9 FINISHING OF METALS

With a metal the final finish is very important. The designer may use this as a form of protection or as a means of decoration. What is vital is that the metal is carefully prepared by cleaning. Remove all working marks – scratches, file marks etc. This is so that the finish that is applied will not be spoiled.

Steels

These are prepared by using finer files for the final shaping of the work. Carefully drawfile until a bright finish is obtained. Emery cloth is then wrapped around the file and rubbed in one direction over the surface. If different grades of emery cloth are used, a very bright finish will result.

This method can be used on non-ferrous metals but does not give the high shine that can come from polishing; it does, however, give a textured finish.

Non-ferrous metals

These are best cleaned by first placing them in a bath of diluted sulphuric acid (1 part acid to 9 parts water). Extreme care has to be taken when doing this. In the acid bath the acid attacks the metal surface, removing dirt, grease

Ⓢ
Hands and face must be kept well clear. Brass tongs must be used to handle the work. Wear goggles.

Why should brass tongs be used and not steel ones?

How can dipping hot metal into an acid bath be dangerous?

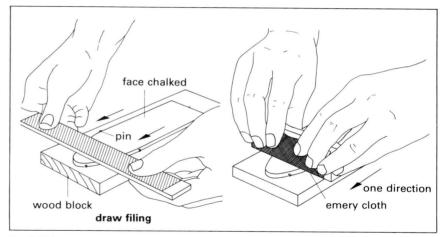

Fig. 2.103

and oxide film. The work is removed after a short time and the acid is washed off. A damp cloth is now dipped into pumice powder and rubbed over the surface to remove the loose dirt (Fig. 2.104).

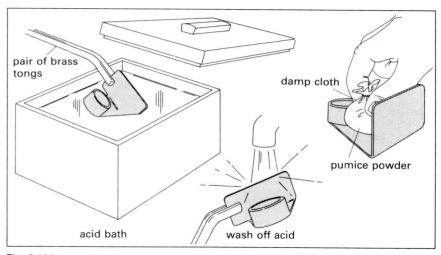

Fig. 2.104

The work is clean but may have scratches. These are removed by using a **water of Ayr stone**. This is dipped in water and rubbed over the work. It is a very fine abrasive, making the marks and scratches disappear. Once they are removed, the work is ready for polishing on another surface decoration.

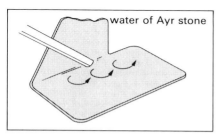

Fig. 2.105

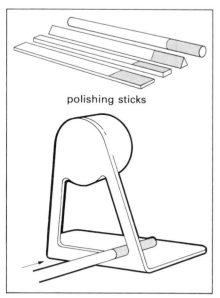

Fig. 2.106

Polishing

This can be done by hand or by machine; the method will depend on how complicated the work is and if it has fine detail.

Hand polishing

This is only used when very small or awkward pieces have to be polished. Little sticks are made up with pieces of suede glued to the tips. A polishing compound is applied to the end and the stick is rubbed briskly over the surface until a high gloss finish is obtained.

Bamboo strips are often used as polishing sticks. Why do you think this is?

Finishing of metals

Machine polishing

A polishing machine uses maps or brushes securely screwed into tapered spindles. Soft felt mops are stiff and quite hard; and are used for work requiring a lot of polishing. Calico mops are circular pieces of the material calico, held together by fibre washers; some are stitched together for coarse work, whilst unstitched ones are used for fine work. Swansdown mops are very soft and are only used for a final high-gloss finish.

The mops are first dressed with polish (a fine grit bedded in a wax bar). Different polishes are used with the mops to give the finish required.

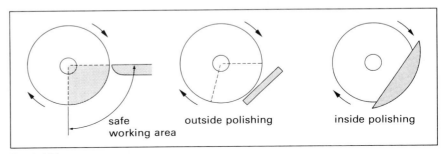

safe working area   outside polishing   inside polishing

Fig. 2.107

The work is pressed against the mop, in the safe working position (Fig. 2.107), until a shine starts to appear. The first mops have to work hard to buff the surface, while the final ones begin to develop the high shine.

> As the work proceeds, the polished metal becomes quite hot. There is a temptation to hold the work in a cloth or apron. This can be dangerous, as they can easily get caught in machines. Use gloves or fix the work to a wooden block.

What do you think would happen if the work was placed on top of the mop?

Most polished metals will need some form of surface protection or they will start to dull and tarnish.

Lacquering

To protect the surface a thin layer of lacquer (cellulose or gum) can be brushed or sprayed over the metal. This will give a transparent coat that will allow the colour of the metal to show through. Use white spirit to de-grease the surface before applying the lacquer. If white spirit is not used, the finish will not stay long; it will flake if the work is handled a great deal. Lacquering is not used for engineering type work, but is used for more decorative work such as jewellery.

Colouring

It is possible to colour metals by dipping or brushing them with certain chemicals. Care has to be taken that it is done in a well-ventilated area and that all chemicals are handled carefully, following the manufacturers' instructions. Various shades of brown can be achieved on copper and brass by dipping them in a weak solution of potassium sulphide or ammonium sulphide. *Green* can be obtained by dipping in a mixture of ammonia and sodium acetate and copper nitrate solution. *Black* can be accomplished by using potassium persulphate. All of these will need lacquering after the colouring to protect the final finish.

Why do you think the colour needs some form of protection?

Aluminium

In its pure state, aluminium can be coloured with dyes. **Anodising** is thickening the natural oxide film on the aluminium. The workpiece is the anode (+) and lead plates are the cathodes (−). They are immersed in a solution of sulphuric acid, sodium sulphate and water. The DC current passes through the solution. The result is a thin oxide skin on the metal. This film is converted by boiling the metal in clean water. It is at this stage that the colouring agent or dye is added. The final surface must be protected by lacquering.

Steel

This can be **blued** by heating the surface until the blue oxide forms. It is then quenched in water. When wiped dry, it can be given a coating of beeswax as a limited form of protection. Steel can also be **blackened** by heating to a blue oxide colour as before, then quenching in a high flashpoint oil. When removed, it is gently dried with a low flame. This burnt oil finish gives a good corrosive resistant surface.

Painting

This not only provides a vast colour range but gives the metal protection. All metals that are to be painted must be oil and grease free; with all traces of rust removed from non-ferrous metals. It has to be rubbed down lightly before the undercoat is applied. This, in turn, is rubbed down before applying the final coat or coats of the required colour.

Plastic coating

This also gives colour and protection to metals. The simple method is to use a thermoplastic powder such as polystyrene, and melt it onto the surface. First clean the metal and heat it evenly to about 180°C, using an oven. Remove the work and plunge quickly into a fluidised bed of plastic powder. Some powder will fuse and stick to the hot metal, giving a thin coating of plastic. Remove and return to the oven to completely fuse the coating.

Enamelling

This type of surface finish uses powdered glass, which is made to melt and flow over the metal. As it is quite hard and very colourful, it gives protection

Masking tape is sometimes used to blank out areas before anodising. What effect do you think this has on the colouring?

Why do you think it is the ferrous metals that are normally painted?

Plastic-coated tools

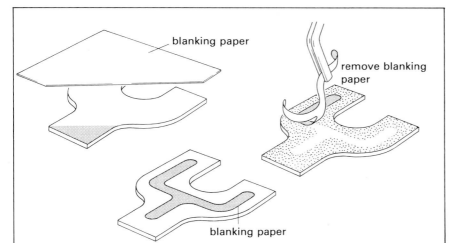

blanking paper

remove blanking paper

blanking paper

Fig. 2.108

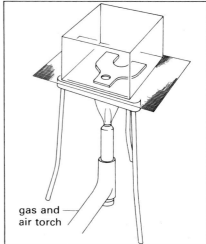

gas and air torch

Fig. 2.109

Why should work that has been soft or silver soldered together present problems?

Enamelling oven

and decoration. It is used on steel items such as cookers, washing machines etc. For more decorative work, copper, gilding metal or silver are used as the base metal.

Before a piece of work can be enamelled the surface must be cleaned in an acid bath and then scoured with pumice powder. Care must be taken not to touch the surface with fingers. The surface is now brushed with a thin adhesive (polycell), which burns away when the heating takes place. The powdered glass is sieved gently over the surface until a layer is formed (the adhesive holds the glass in place).

The work is now heated to about 750°C in a special oven or by playing a gas and air torch under the work. The glass melts quickly and flows over the surface. Afterwards, the work is allowed to cool.

If a further design is needed, part of the work can be blanked out with paper or a stencil. Adhesive is again used and the second colour is added. The paper is carefully removed and the work is reheated. The two colours melt and flow together.

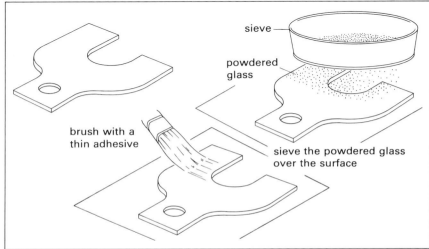

Fig. 2.110

The ways the colours are applied in enamelling can vary according to the technique used. The two most common methods are *champlevé* and *cloisonné*.

Champlevé

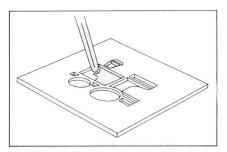

Fig. 2.111   Champlevé

This method uses etching grooves or other means to make depressions in the metal. These are then filled with powdered glass, which can be any colour. The work is heated or fired. In this way, the glass flow is limited and a more accurate design can be built up.

Cloisonné

In this method the design is built up with thin wire, embedded in a base coat of enamel. The little enclosed spaces that are made by the wire are filled with the other colours and again fired.

Electroplating

This is a surface finish that gives a base metal a coating of another protective or decorative metal. For example, our copper watch stand can be made quite cheaply, and a very thin coating of silver will make it look very expensive. Electroplating is a similar method to anodising, except that the work itself is the cathode (−) The work is suspended in a solution − an appropriate metallic salt (electrolyte) which acts as a conductor. A plate or rod of the metal to be deposited acts as the anode. The direct current is passed through the set up, and the transfer takes place. This system does not hide faults such as scratches, marks etc, but highlights them.

Etching

If a design or pattern has to be made on a surface, one way is to use acids. These attack any exposed metal, eating deeper into the metal the longer they are left together. The designer covers the polished work with an acid-resisting substance, such as paraffin wax. The design is then drawn on to the

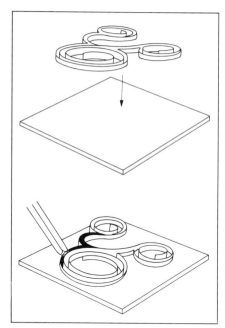
Fig. 2.112 Cloisonné

The powdered glass is sometimes mixed with glue before it is applied. Can you think why?

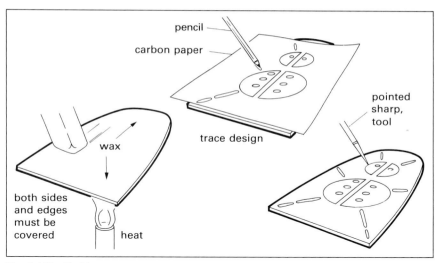
Fig. 2.113 Etching

surface by using carbon paper and tracing through. The traced design is scratched out carefully with sharp pointed tools. If the work is small it can be dipped into a bath of nitric acid and left for the acid to work on the metal. If the work is large, the acid can be placed inside and brushed back and forth with a feather. It is safer to use ferric chloride for this type of work. The acid leaves a fine textured finish. The wax is removed and the final surface is lacquered.

When the work is put into the acid bath it is never laid flat. Why do you think this is?

3.1 SOURCES AND STRUCTURES OF PLASTICS

We all tend to use the word 'plastic' to cover any of the vast range of man-made materials produced and used in place of natural materials. They do, however, differ greatly from hard and brittle to soft and flexible; from those that will melt to those that can stand high temperatures. They are not just cheap substitutes but are working materials that can offer a unique range of properties.

Plastics are derived from two main sources:

1. Natural resources such as animals, plants, insects and trees which give us naturally occurring plastics e.g. celluloid and cellophane which are derived from cotton wool and casein glue from cow's milk. All are modified forms of the natural material. They play only a small part in the plastics industry.

2. Synthetic plastics are made from breaking down crude oil, natural gas and coal into usable parts, then rejoining them in different forms. It is the synthetic plastics that make up the major part of the plastics we use in our everyday lives, and it has been the chemist who has been able to build up a workable and useful material.

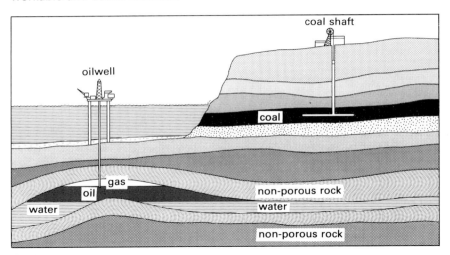

Fig. 3.1

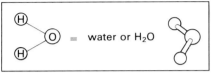

Fig. 3.2

The chemist works on the principle that all matter can be broken down into elements; with plastics these are carbon, hydrogen, oxygen, nitrogen, fluorine and chlorine. When the elements are in their smallest form (atoms), they can be combined to form the many materials and polymers. For example, if we add two hydrogen atoms to one oxygen atom, we create water, or rather one *molecule* of water (see Fig. 3.2). We have changed two gases into a liquid.

With most plastics the major element is carbon; this can form bonds with four atoms at one time to create methane. Therefore, carbon has a **valency** of four.

In plastics, however, the molecules do not stay as single units, but link up with others to form long chains or giant molecules. The small unit forming the link in the chain is known as the **monomer**. The linking is called **polymerisation**. This is why so many plastics have poly in their name; polyethylene, polystyrene, polyester.

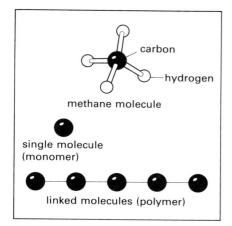

carbon

hydrogen

methane molecule

single molecule
(monomer)

linked molecules (polymer)

Fig. 3.3

To obtain the basic elements, crude oil has to be refined or separated. This takes place inside a **fractionating tower** (Fig. 3.4), by heating the oil and changing it to gases. As the gases rise inside the tower they pass through trays of liquid. This causes separation or breaking into fractions. Some of the refined fractions are cleaned and used as they are e.g. camping gas, aviation fuel and heating oil. The fraction used for making the plastics is **naphtha**, a straw-coloured liquid made up of carbon and hydrogen.

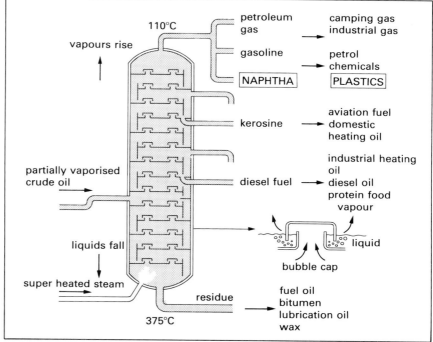

Fig. 3.4 Fractionating tower

Why do the gases condense back to liquids at the different stages?

Naphtha is heated with steam inside a furnace. This breaks up the structure or cracks it into fragments. The two important fragments being ethylene and propylene.

How the linking takes place

What material have we formed by linking the single molecule of ethylene?

The methane molecule with its single carbon atom holding four hydrogen atoms is a stable compound. It is said to be **saturated** as it is unable to take more atoms and can only be changed by substituting atoms. If a compound has one or more carbon atoms linked chemically by double (or triple) bonds, it is unstable or **unsaturated**. These compounds are ideal for linking together to form the polymer chains. Ethylene is a double-bonded molecule. A single molecule of ethylene has two carbon atoms which each hold two hydrogen atoms and link to each other. The two curved links represent the weakness of the molecule. It is this weakness that the chemist uses: by first breaking one of the double bonds, each carbon atom is free to link up with another similar broken molecule.

In this way, the long chains are formed – made up of several thousand atoms. This is known as an **addition reaction**. As the chains form they become entangled with each other, because the atoms do not join in neat

Sources and structures of plastics

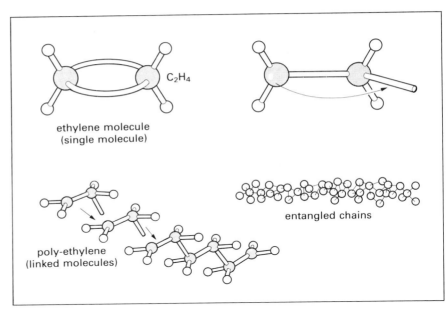

Fig. 3.5

lines. The chains bond together by weak electronic forces called **Van der Waals**, and so form solid but plastic material.

This linking of the chains is how most **thermoplastics** are formed. All that needs to be done is to heat the plastic. This makes the atoms vibrate and moves the linked chains apart. As the chains untangle, the material becomes soft and pliable. It can now be shaped easily. On cooling, the chains reposition themselves; the material returns to a solid state.

Plastics or polymers can also be formed by joining different types of monomers; for example, a molecule of *urea* could be joined to a molecule of *formaldehyde*. Before the two can join, an atom or atoms have to be removed. This is done by forming a molecule of water by **condensation polymerisation**. One oxygen atom and two hydrogen atoms are thus eliminated. Chains can again be formed. In some cases they may start to form a more rigid network system.

Thermoplastic – PVC

Fig. 3.6

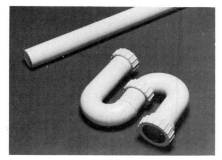

Drainage pipes

Why would leaving the lid off some plastic materials cause them to go off?

From this we can obtain thermoplastics and the thermosetting plastics. It is the **thermosetting plastics** that take up the network form, linking together as a rigid molecular structure. Once they are formed and hard they cannot be reheated and changed.

Other additions are sometimes mixed with the polymer molecules, to help or improve them in some way. **Catalyses** are added to either increase or decrease the speed at which the molecules link up. This can be useful when time is important and a quicker setting reaction is needed, as in casting. Another monomer may set too quickly or be affected by light, giving little time to work the material; this has to be slowed down. **Plasticisers** are normally liquids. They are added to polymers to make them less brittle and to lower their softening temperatures. A good example is polyvinyl chloride (PVC), which is a hard and stiff plastic and can be seen in this form as drain pipes. When an oily plasticiser is added, it becomes soft and flexible and can be used for such things as wallcoverings and packaging. **Fillers** are powdered solids that are added to polymers, but do not mix chemically. They can reduce the brittleness and increase the impact strength. They also help to reduce the cost by using less polymer. Other fillers can increase the heat or chemical resistance of a plastic.

3.2 THERMOSETTING AND THERMOPLASTICS

As you will see from Table 11 overleaf a very wide range of plastics could be used for our watch stand;

polyester resin – hard and strong when reinforced with glass fibre;

ABS – excellent strength and finish, but only in powder or granules;

polypropylene – light and strong in sheet, powder or granules;

acrylic – light and rigid, with good colour in sheet, rod or tube.

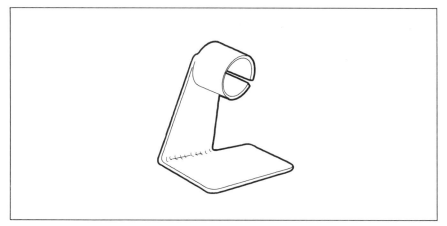

Fig. 3.7

Plastic	Trade names	Different forms
Thermosetting plastics Phenolic resin	Bakelite	powder, granules, reinforced laminates
Polyester resin	Beetle Orel	liquids, pastes
Epoxy resin (Epoxide)	Araldite	liquids, pastes
Melamine-formaldehyde resin	Formica Melaware	laminates, granules, powder
Polyurethane	Suprasec Daltolac	rigid and flexible foams, coatings
Urea-formaldehyde resin	Aerolite Cascomite	powder, syrup, granules
Thermoplastics Acrylonitrile-Butadeine Styrene (ABS)	Cycolac	powder, granules
Polyvinyl chloride (PVC)	Corvic Welvic	(rigid form) – powder, pastes (flexible form) – powders, pastes, liquids, sheet
Polymethyl methacrylate (acrylic)	Perspex Diakon	sheet, rod, tube
Polyamide (nylon)	Maranyl Kapton	powder, granules, rod, tube, sheet
Polythene or polyethylene	Rigidex	(hard) – powder, granules, sheet
	Alkathene Visqueen	(soft) – powder, film, sheet
Polystyrene	Lustrex Styron	powders, granules, sheet expanded foam, beads, slabs
Polypropylene	Propathene	powders, granules, sheet
Polytetrafluoroethene	Teflon Fluon	powder
Cellulose acetate	Dexel	powder, film, sheet, rod

Table 11

3 Plastics

Properties	Uses
Strength, hardness and ridigity; can be produced at low cost; colours limited to black or brown	Pan handles, knobs, electrical switch covers, appliance parts
Good surface hardness; can be formed without heat and pressure	Light switches, tuning devices, coatings, structural coverings (when reinforced with glass fibres) e.g. boat hulls, car bodies etc.
Exceptional adhesive qualities with low shrinkage; high strength when reinforced	As a bonding agent, encapsulating, surface coating, laminating
Low water absorption; tasteless, odourless; resists scratching and marking	Tableware, buttons, distributor heads, laminated surfaces (e.g. table tops), industrial baking enamel, cookers, refrigerators
Weather resistant even though colour changes; high tear resistance	(rigid) – insulating material, floats (flexible) – upholstery, mattresses, paint
Stiff and hard with good adhesive qualities	Adhesives, laminating timber, coating of paper and textiles, electrical fittings
Excellent impact and scratch resistance; good strength, lightness and durability; high surface finish	Kitchenware, clock and camera cases, toys (Lego), crash helmets
Strong with good abrasive resistance; low moisture absorption; good chemical resistance	(rigid) – pipes, plumbing fittings, corrugated roofing (flexible) – packaging, textiles, upholstery
Excellent light transmission qualities; hard and rigid; takes colour well;	Display signs and cases, lenses, dials, furniture, jewellery
Very good resistance to temperature extremes; tough and mechanically durable; high chemical resistance	Gears, bearings, washers, bristles, textiles, clothing, stockings, upholstery
Good resistance to breakage; withstands low temperatures	(rigid) – household wares e.g. buckets, bowls (flexible) – bags for food, bottles, electrical cable coating
Transparent, but colours well; (with rubber) impact resistance	Food containers, lamp shades, toys, model kits, yogurt cartons
Light, buoyant; good insulation	Packaging, insulation
Higher density and more rigid than polythene; very light; good chemical resistance	Crates, chair seats, ropes, plumbing fittings, kitchenware
Resistance to high temperatures; strength; hard; good friction qualities	Coatings, non-lubricated bearings, gaskets, heating cable, plumbers' tape
Hard but tough; can be made flexible	Photographic film, packaging, spectacle frames, toothbrush handles

Thermosetting and thermoplastics

3.3 TESTING PLASTICS

Simple identification tests

Because many of the plastics look so similar, it is sometimes necessary to determine the correct type. It is possible to identify most by simple workshop tests; e.g. cutting, scratching, burning. See Fig. 3.8 for simple identification tests.

> **S** Care should be taken to use safety gloves and tongs to avoid burning from dripping plastic. The fumes given off may be poisonous so extreme care must be taken when testing; make sure the room is well ventilated. The sample should be removed from the flame before the smell test is carried out.

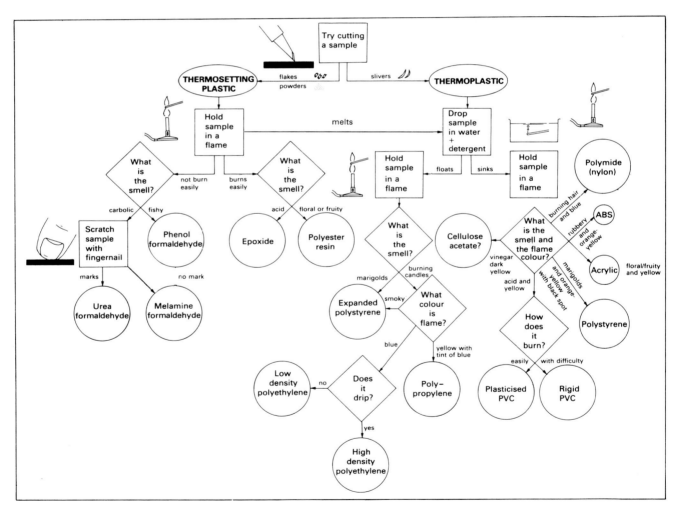

Fig. 3.8

3.4 SHAPING PLASTICS — CASTING, MOULDING, FORMING AND BENDING

Casting plastic

It is possible to use plastics materials when they are in a liquid state to form complicated shapes when poured into moulds. On curing or setting, the plastic will give an exact copy of the mould shape.

Tray casting

This is the very simplest form of casting, using thermoplastic powders such as polythene and ABS. The mould is a very shallow tray of metal, in which tiles or panels can be formed.

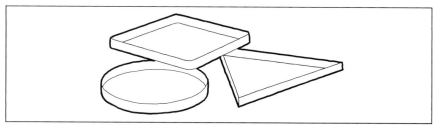

Fig. 3.9   Metal trays

Why do you think metal is used as the mould?

Lightly grease or oil the mould, to provide a release agent for the tile shape. The tray is then filled with colour powder or granules, until the mould is full and level at the top. It is placed in an oven and heated for a few minutes at about 200°C; so melting the plastic powder. The plastic sinks slightly and forms the tray shape. On cooling, the coloured tile can be removed from the mould.

Fig. 3.10

Further design shape can now be added to the surface as an extension of the work.

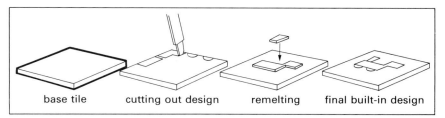

Fig. 3.11

Shaping plastics

Cold casting

This form of casting uses the thermosetting plastics. Once the shape is formed it cannot be changed or worked by heat. The two main types of plastic used are polyester resin (unsaturated) and epoxy resin. Both are used in a liquid state. To activate the setting process (polymerisation) a catalyst has to be mixed with the resin. The resin manufacturer may recommend the use of an accelerator, to speed up the setting time.

 It is very important to keep the catalyst and accelerator well apart during storage. They can react violently when mixed together. They must only be used as recommended by the manufacturer. All resin work must be done in a well-ventilated room due to the fumes given off – and handled with care, using rubber gloves.

The mould can be made from a wide range of materials e.g. paraffin wax, aluminium foil, rubber, glass, polythene or plaster. Only polystyrene is unsuitable, due to the chemical reaction with the resin which causes it to dissolve. The mould material will tend to be chosen by the shape that has to be formed; for example, if a simple round block is needed then a polythene bottle could be cut down to size and used. If a more detailed mould is needed then a shape could be cut out of a block of wax.

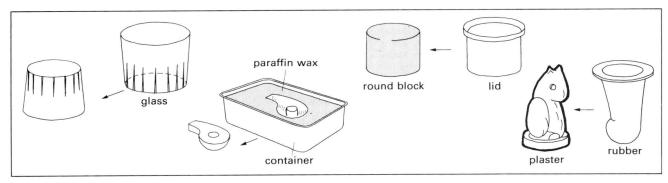

Fig. 3.12

Why would a disposable plastic cup or a yogurt carton be of little use as a mould?

A more complicated shape, such as our watch stand, needs to have a master pattern made from a suitable material, coated with a release agent. This is set in a mould box, and plaster is poured around the pattern and allowed to set. A more flexible mould material can be used, such as rubber, silicone, remeltable PVC. Once the mould material has set, the pattern is removed and the mould is ready for use. (The mould could also be made by vacuum forming around a pattern.)

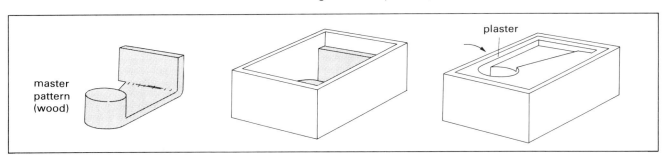

Fig. 3.13

The casting process

To cast with the resin, the mould has to be first coated with release agent. Sufficient resin to fill the mould is mixed with a colouring pigment, if needed, and the correct number of catalyst drops. A good guide to the amount of resin needed is to first fill the mould with water and use this amount as the measure. (The mould will then need to be dried.) Once the resin and catalyst are mixed, pour them carefully into the mould, and gently stir to remove all air pockets. When the resin starts to gel, the object is eased from the mould and placed on a flat surface (e.g. glass) for final setting to take place.

At this final stage, further coloured resins may be poured into any small cavities or grooves to complete a design. Sometimes fillers are used to reduce the amount of resin needed; for example, aluminium oxide can reduce shrinkage and give added strength. The casting formed is hard and brittle.

How do fillers help to reduce the cost of casting?

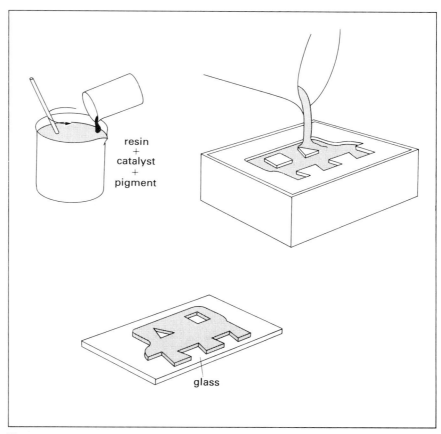

resin
+
catalyst
+
pigment

glass

Fig. 3.14

Clear resin casting can be used for encasing an object that is delicate or has to be preserved. This is called **encapsulation** or **embedding**. It is used a great deal for items that have to be displayed or handled. The process is similar to casting, except that it is done in stages or layers, until the object is covered. Great care has to be taken to keep the object and each layer clean and free from dust or dirt. The mould is filled to about a quarter of its depth, and allowed to set or cure. The hardened resin has a sticky surface on to which the object is placed. Such things as flowers and leaves must be treated with a preservative, or dried and sprayed with clear varnish. They are allowed to sink into the resin while soft. Once the object is in place more clear resin is added and allowed to cure (see Fig. 3.15).

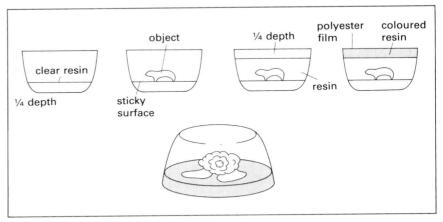

Fig. 3.15

Why should dust and dirt be a problem when clear casting?

The final layer can be coloured resin, as it is the base. A thin sheet of polyester film is now placed on the setting resin to stop it from becoming sticky. Once cured the cast object can be removed, cleaned, rubbed down with wet and dry paper and polished if needed.

Injection moulding

This is one of the major methods of shaping thermoplastic material in industry and schools. The powder or granules are heated until soft. They are then forced under pressure or injected into a mould. The shape is removed when cool.

Such things as buckets, bowls, safety helmets and toys are a few of the many items made using this method. A wide range of thermoplastics can be used — polythene, ABS, PVC, nylon, polypropylene, polystyrene. The only

Which plastic do you think has been used to mould the shapes shown in the photos?

Fig. 3.16

drawback with this system is the size of moulding machine available: most school machines are quite small; this limits what can be produced.

Our watch stand could be made in this way, but the size of moulding machine available would probably prevent it being made in school.

In the injection mould system skill is necessary in designing and making the mould. Once made and proved successful, the mould can produce thousands of the items very quickly. The mould is usually made of metal — steel is the main material due to the amount of pressure that is involved, although epoxy resin can be used. The mould is made in two halves, but can be built up from a number of pieces. The matching faces of the mould have the design shape cut into the surface. These faces have to be flat and accurate or the plastic will leak or flash from the mould. Guide pins link the two halves together (Fig. 3.17).

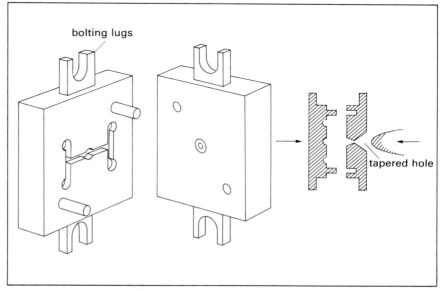

Fig. 3.17   A simple mould

If a piece of work has a thin film of material rounds its edges, what is wrong with the mould?

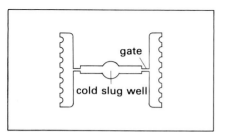

Fig. 3.18

A tapered hole or sprue is made in one half of the mould, for the plastic to enter. In the opposite half a basin is formed, sometimes called a *cold slug well*, into which the soft plastic first flows. From this it runs along cut channels or runners, until just before entering the shape cut out. Here it is restricted by a narrow *gate* (Fig. 3.18). This allows the material formed by the sprue and runners to be broken off once the work is finished. In this way only a tiny mark shows on the finished item.

Several types of gate are used. This is to enable the best possible flow of plastic to form the shape desired.

Sprue gate – used when it is possible to flow the plastic directly into the shape without spoiling the appearance; for example, into the bottom of the bucket as this will not be seen when in use.

Pin gate – used when the sides of an object are very thin and the break-off needs to be as small as possible.

Side gate – the standard type of gate when a number of mouldings are being made together from one runner; for example, a model kit with many different pieces.

Ring gate – used when the shape has a hollow or hole, so the plastic is made to flow round a central core.

For any mould to be successful the runners should have no sharp corners, allowing the plastic to flow evenly.

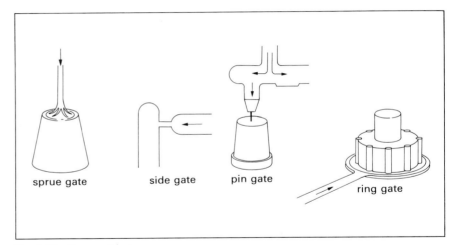

Fig. 3.19 Types of gate

How the moulding is done

Once the mould is made up, it is bolted or clamped to an injection moulding machine: one half to the nozzle face, the other to the locking system face.

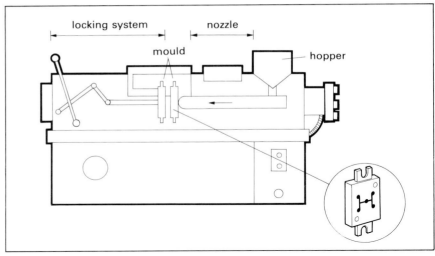

Fig. 3.20 Injection moulder

The granules of plastic are put into a hopper at the top of the machine, which feeds them down into the barrel. Inside the barrel is a revolving screw, which carries the plastic forward towards the nozzle. Around the barrel are band heaters that soften the plastic as it travels along. The temperature will vary according to the thermoplastic being used: PVC – 180°C; polystyrene – 200°C; nylon – 290°C.

As the softened plastic builds up, it forces the screw backwards until it stops rotating; it is now ready for use. The mould is closed up and locked by a hydraulic ram. Hydraulic pressure is also applied to the screw forcing it forward. This pushes the softened plastic through the nozzle hole into the mould. After cooling for a few seconds the mould is opened and the shape removed. This process can now be repeated, so that many similar items can be produced in this way.

A cold mould can sometimes affect the filling up of a mould with plastic. Can you think why?

3 Plastics

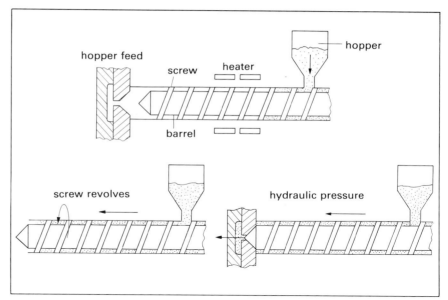

Fig. 3.21

Compression moulding

This system is used for shaping thermosetting plastics such as phenol-formaldehyde and urea-formaldehyde resins, when they are in powdered form. The powder is subjected to intense heat and pressure. This starts the cross-linking of atoms from the hard thermosetting material. A measured amount of powder is placed inside the bottom half of the mould. The top half

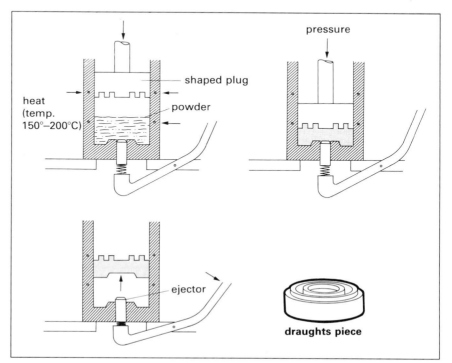

Fig. 3.22

Why would thermoplastic be of little use for making the electrical items named?

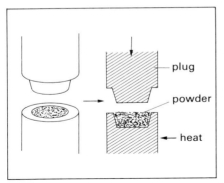

Fig. 3.23

Why do you think a sharp corner causes the plastic to thin out at this point?

of the mould closes under pressure, while the mould heats up. As the plastic softens, the pressure of the top half of the mould or ram forces it to take up the design shape in the bottom half of the mould. On cooling, the plastic sets very hard. It can be removed or ejected from the mould. Such items as electric light and power sockets, electric iron handles, electric cooker controls and ash trays are made in this way.

In schools, simple moulds can be made up in the form of steel cylinder shapes. They are normally in three parts: the cylindrical body which will contain the powder and house the mould and ram; the mould which contains the design or shape; and the ram which is a good sliding fit with the body and compresses the powder. All of these need to be highly polished to give the best finish possible. It does, however, require the use of a compression moulding machine to obtain the controlled pressure and temperature when using the mould.

Vacuum forming

Intricate shapes and designs can be formed by heating a thin thermoplastic sheet until it is in a softened state; then drawing it over or into a shaped mould using an air vacuum. Such things as trays, dishes, masks, relief maps etc can be made in this way. Most of the common thermoplastics can be used: polythene, PVC, polystyrene, ABS – ranging from 0.025mm to 6.35mm thickness. It is only the size of the machine that limits the size and shape of the work that is possible, as it needs uniform heating and the correct amount of vacuum.

The mould or design shape

This will determine how successful the final work can be. The forming can be completed in two different ways:
1. *a female mould* into which the plastic sheet is drawn, giving a very good internal finish. It tends to thin the sheet as it forms the shape.
2. *a male mould* is a raised shape on to which the plastic sheet is drawn, giving a very good external finish with an even thickness.

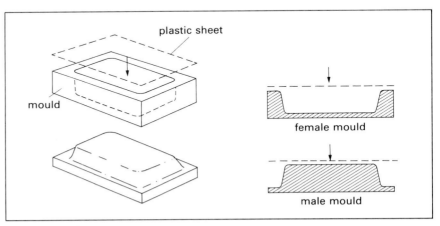

Fig. 3.24

The moulds are designed to a slight taper on their depth, and have all sharp corners rounded. This allows the formed shape to be removed easily and helps the plastic to flow to the outline without thinning.

The other major detail in vacuum forming is that the mould is given small air vents in any awkward positions, such as dips or hollows, where air could

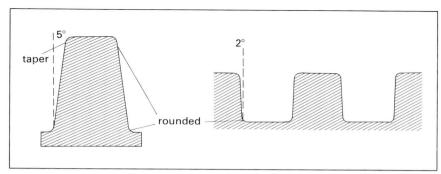

Fig. 3.25

Why do you think the tiny air holes could affect the final work?

get trapped. The tiny air holes help the plastic to follow the shape, by allowing a vacuum to take place inside the mould as well as around the outside. The holes are kept small so that they do not spoil the final appearance of the work.

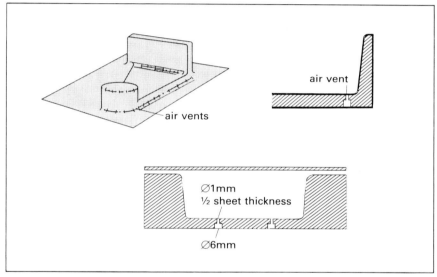

Fig. 3.26

The mould can be made from any material that can stand up to the slight pressure and heat. It should have a smooth surface to give the best possible finish, free from marks and faults that could show up on the plastic.

Wood – an ideal mould material; easy to shape and join together into complicated items. However, it can twist and warp with the heat over a period of time, so it does have a limited life.

Metal – much more difficult to shape, but can be used in a cast aluminium form made from a wooden pattern. It needs to be slightly warm before use, which helps the shaping process. It has a long life as a mould and it is only the time taken in making the original mould that is disadvantageous.

Plaster – a very useful modelling material; allows difficult shapes to be made up quickly and easily. It has the advantage of being porous so it does not require as many vent holes. However, it is weak and easily broken; and can crack with the heat.

Epoxy resin – like aluminium, can be cast into shape, giving an excellent detailed mould. It can, however, be affected by heat unless the surface is protected by spraying with a metal alloy.

Once the mould is made, it is placed on the vacuum machine table (Fig. 3.27) ready for forming.

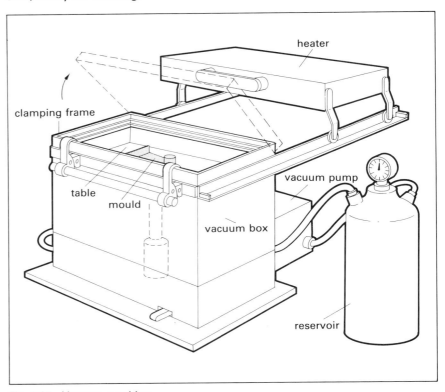

Fig. 3.27   Vacuum machine

The vacuum machine

This consists of (a) a clamping frame for holding the thermoplastic sheet firmly in place while it is heated and formed; (b) a heater that may be fixed or movable – ranging in size from 10 to 30kw/m^2 so that different types and thicknesses of sheeting can be used; (c) a vacuum box that is connected to a vacuum pump and reservoir, so that all air can be removed quickly as forming takes place; (d) a table on which the mould rests while the plastic forms around it.

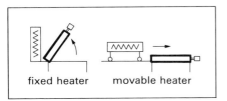

Fig. 3.28

What do you think would happen if the sheet was not soft when the vacuum starts?

The moulding process

This can be done in three different ways:

1. *Female forming* – the mould is set up on the table in a central position, resting on small scrap pieces of thermoplastic (this helps the vacuum round the base of the mould). The thermoplastic sheet is clamped in position over the mould. The heater applies heat to the plastic surface, causing it to soften and sag. Once this happens the heater is removed and the vacuum activated. Atmospheric pressure forces the soft plastic sheet down into the mould, forming the shape. However, the sheet does tend to thin near the clamping points, due to stretching. It is limited to fairly shallow work.

2. *Male forming* – or sometimes called box forming – starts in the same way as female forming, with the mould on the table and the plastic sheet held and heated until soft. The vacuum is again applied, but this time the sheet is forced down and around the outside of the mould. This tends to use more material, but does give a much better overall sheet thickness.

3   Plastics

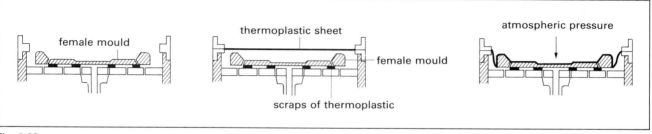

Fig. 3.29

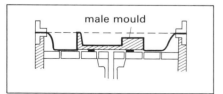

Fig. 3.30

3. *Drape forming* – can be done with either the male or the female former. The difference is that the mould is brought up into the softened sheet by a piston-assisted ram. The sheet drapes itself over the mould partly forming the shape; the vacuum is then activated to complete the work. In this way, it is possible to make deep shapes without thinning the sheet unevenly.

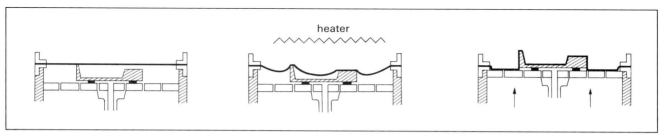

Fig. 3.31   Drape forming

Press forming

How can a cold mould affect the drape method of forming?

This is another method of shaping sheet material. Simple formers are used, which are the inside and outside of the final shape. The sheet of the thermoplastic is heated in an oven, then quickly removed with tongs and clamped over the inside or female former. The male former is pressed down, pushing the sheet into shape.

This method works quite well but can cause marks on the surface of the sheet, due to the male former touching the plastic. It can also cause the plastic to stretch unevenly, thinning in places.

Why do you think a small gap is left between the two matching formers?

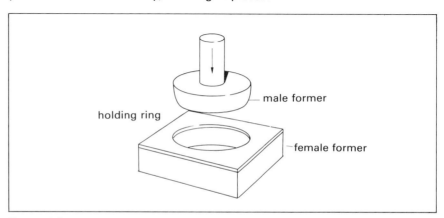

Fig. 3.32(a)   Press forming

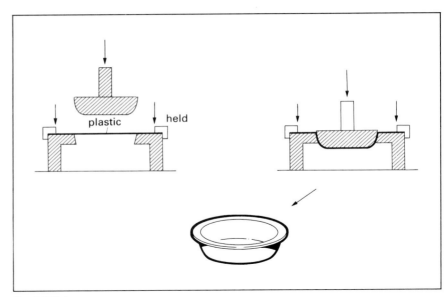

Fig. 3.32(b)

Blow moulding

What could the dome shape be used for in a design situation?

This method also uses thermoplastic sheet material in a softened state. It shapes the thermoplastic by blowing compressed air onto the surface. The sheet is trapped on a flat surface or table. Compressed air is blown through a narrow inlet, pushing the sheet into a large dome shape. On cooling, the plastic hardens into this form.

The size of the dome can be controlled by the size of the clamping frame which will give the diameter of the base. Its height can be controlled by the volume of air allowed through the inlet.

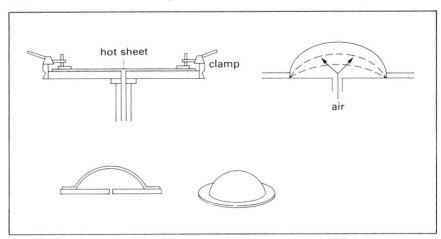

Fig. 3.33

Further shapes can be made if some form of stop or restriction is placed above the sheet, so that as the dome forms it is limited. In this way, the dome can be given a flat top or a hollow as it takes up the restricted shape (see Fig. 3.34).

A more advanced system is to blow the sheet material into a shaped mould. This means that more complicated shapes are possible. The softened

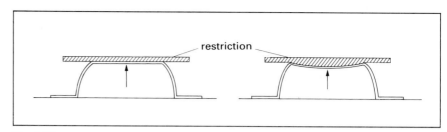

Fig. 3.34

Why should the compressed air be warm?

sheet of thermoplastic is clamped over a hollow or cavity mould by means of a sealing plate. Compressed air is now blown onto the sheet, stretching it into the mould shape.

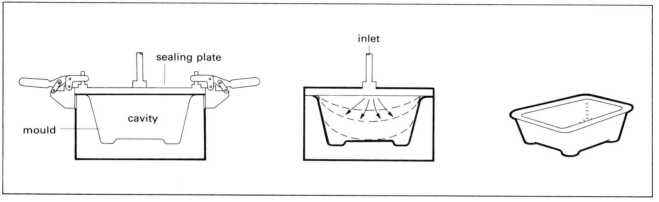

Fig. 3.35

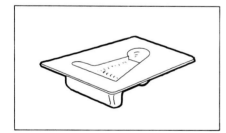

Fig. 3.36

Our watch stand could be made by this method. Why is it unsuitable?

Industry uses this system, using tube form plastic, for making bottles and containers. The thermoplastic tube is extruded (see page 142) between two halves of a mould. The mould closes together, sealing the bottom of the tube and cutting it to the required length. In this form, it is called a *parison*. The mould is repositioned under a compressed air nozzle. Air is blown into the soft parison, making it form the mould shape. The plastic cools on contact with the cold mould surface. When the mould re-opens, the blown shape falls out and the cycle starts again.

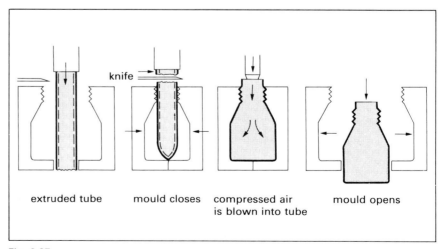

Fig. 3.37

Shaping plastics

Hot bending

Acrylic sheet can be reheated and softened many times without any ill effects. This makes it an ideal material for shaping in the workshop, with simple heating equipment. By heating the acrylic in a controlled way, it is possible to bend it into simple or complicated shapes. On cooling, the plastic will harden into the formed design.

The acrylic sheet or strip can be heated in two ways:

1. *strip heater* – a simple box system which contains a single electric fire element. The top of the box has a narrow slot or strip, through which the heat can pass in a narrow band. By placing the acrylic on small supports over the slot, a bend area can be softened. The work is turned over at intervals to give equal heating to each side. Once softened, the acrylic bends easily at the heated point while the remaining plastic is quite cold and hard. Care has to be taken not to overheat the plastic and bubble the surface. REMEMBER: make an allowance for the bend by adding the thickness of the sheet to the length.

A bend is always marked on acrylic sheet with a special chinagraph pencil as a normal pencil will not mark. Why is a metal scriber not used?

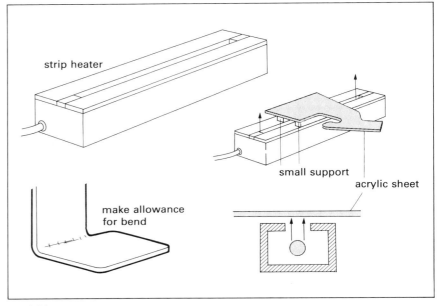

Fig. 3.38

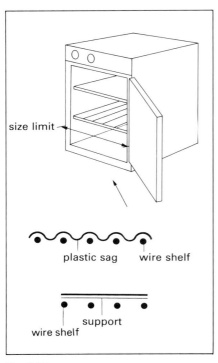

Fig. 3.39

2. *oven heating* – if the work is quite thick, or has more than one bend to form at one time, it will need much more uniform heating than a strip heater can provide. An old domestic oven may be used. The whole of the work is heated to the same temperature: with acrylic, this is about 150°–170°C. In this way, no stress is added to the final object.

As most ovens have shelves that are made in a mesh design, some flat metal sheet has to be placed on top, covered with aluminium foil, to act as a support for the softened plastic. Shaping has to be done quickly before cooling starts to take place. This form of heating is also used for softening plastic for press forming and blow moulding.

 The plastic has to be removed from the oven with care as it will be quite hot: gloves or tongs need to be used.

Bending over a former

Before any bending can be done a simple copy of the shape required has to be prepared. Wood is the best material as it can be shaped quickly and will not chill the acrylic sheet before it has had time to form the bend. The former

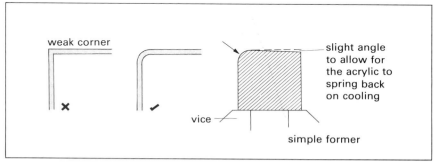

Fig. 3.40

is given slightly rounded corners to allow the plastic to flow and form strong corners. It is also made with a smaller bend angle, to allow for the acrylic spring back on cooling.

The former is now held steady in a vice so that the bending can start. The acrylic work which has now been softened is placed on the former, and can be pressed round easily with gloved hands. It is held in position until cooling takes place, and the acrylic has become hard.

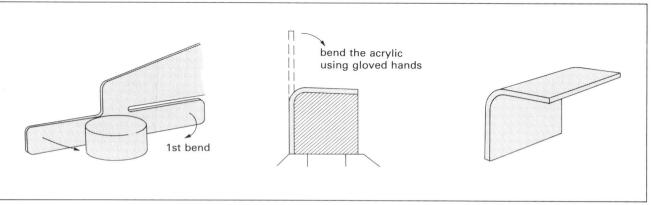

Fig. 3.41

If more than one item is to be made, a bending fixture or jig will need to be made up so that accurate matching shapes are produced. This will help to locate the hot plastic quickly and may provide the bending system.

What method of heating would you use if a strip of acrylic had to be twisted?

A simple bending fixture that could be used for our watch stand is shown in Fig. 3.42.

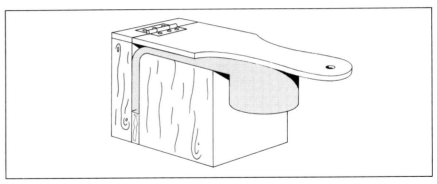

Fig. 3.42   Fixture

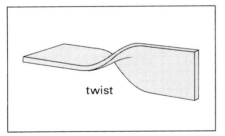

Fig. 3.43

To finish the acrylic shape, it can be rubbed down with a fine grade wet-and-dry abrasive paper to remove any small marks. It can then be polished on a metalworkers' polishing or buffing machine using a mild abrasive and mop. A high-gloss finish can be obtained by careful hand polishing with a suitable liquid acrylic polish.

3.5 SHAPING PLASTICS — LAMINATION, CUTTING, INDUSTRIAL PROCESSES

Lamination

Most of the thermosetting plastics set into hard but brittle materials, which have limited use. They can, however, be converted into strong, tough materials by using them with another material as reinforcement in a sandwich or lamination form. This is simply layers of materials bonded together with resin.

Paper and cloth

These are some of the cheaper materials used for lamination. Sheets of paper or cloth are impregnated with phenolic or melamine resin and allowed to dry. If the laminate is to be a decorative sheet, for example a kitchen

What is the advantage of using this type of laminate for a kitchen work surface?

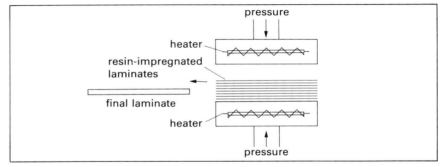

Fig. 3.44

worktop (e.g. Formica), the top sheet has the design printed on and is then impregnated with clear melamine resin. The dried sheets can be stored or used immediately by placing them in a heated press. Pressure and heat (150°C) are now applied to bond the single sheets or laminates into one unit. Such things as kitchen worktops, electrical circuit boards and tea trays are made in this way.

Glass

This is perhaps the best known form of lamination, in which glass fibres are used as a reinforcing material. This method, however, does not use any pressure or heat to form the bonding. Glass Reinforced Plastic (GRP) has great strength – with a hard-wearing surface – yet is normally thin in section and very light.

The glass fibres are made up in different forms to provide for various shapes, strengths, and quality of finish. The cheapest form, with the least strength, is glass cut up into strands and pressed together. This is called chopped strand glass. It is best used for filling or building up work, using another type of glass form to provide the stronger finish.

Why do you think glass fibres are used to reinforce the plastic, and not, for example, metal wire?

The glass fibres can be woven into stronger forms, such as cloth, tape etc. These are more expensive. They are sold by weight – 600gm, 450gm and 300gm per square metre – and come in roll form.

The plastics used are the thermosetting types e.g. polyester and epoxy resin. They are mixed as in cold casting with a catalyst added before the accelerator. This is known as the **lay-up** material or resin, and forms the bonding system with the glass.

The mould

Why do you think it is important that the mould should have a well-finished surface?

To form the design shape a mould has to be made up around which the lamination can be formed. A suitable material (e.g. wood, plaster, clay or a GRP object) could be used. The mould can be either an outside shape (male) or an inside shape (female). What decides the shape to be used is which face of the object is to have the best finish. The face next to the mould gives the best finish; while the other side is quite coarse and shows the glass fibres.

Fig. 3.45

What problems can you foresee if we try to form our watch stand as shown in Fig. 3.46?

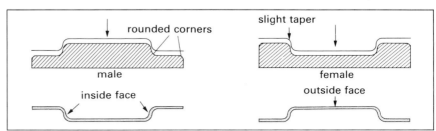

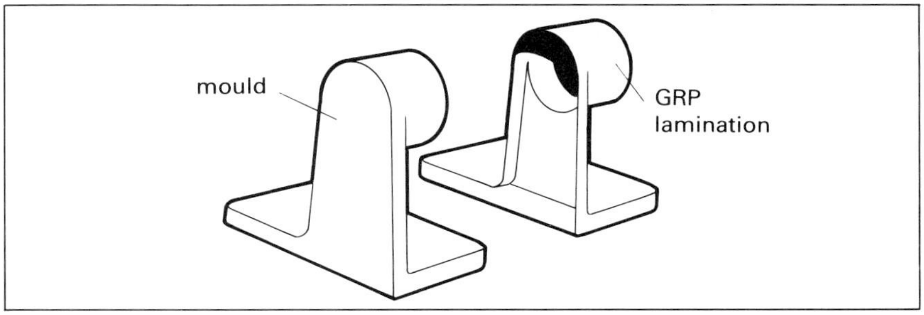

What type of design work would GRP be used for?

Fig. 3.46

Shaping plastics

Forming the lamination

The first stage is to cut the glass fibre mat to the mould shape. This may be a single piece or several pieces for forming a more difficult shape. An allowance of about 25mm is added for overlapping the edges or at joins. It is normal for two layers of matting to be used.

Give the mould a coating with a release agent, normally a wax emulsion. Once dry the gel-coat resin is mixed with a catalyst and colour pigment, which foams into a thick paste. Brush this over the mould surface. Continue until about 1mm thick all over. Leave the resin to partially set or cure. Mix the next layer of resin, the lay-up coat, and brush over the surface. Lay in the first layer of matting and stipple into the resin. This process continues until the required thickness is built up. Then leave to set or cure. The shape can be trimmed around the edges with a sharp knife while it is in the semi-cured state e.g. gel form.

All the tools and brushes that have been used must be quickly cleaned in acetone or another suitable cleaner, before the resin hardens.

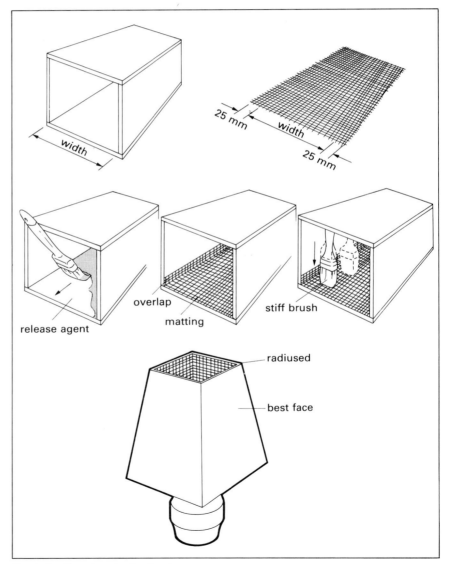

Fig. 3.47   Forming the lamination

Carbon

This is a very recent and important development in strengthening plastics. Spun carbon fibres are made up in the form of cord or 'tow'. The carbon fibres can be laminated to give a strength as high as steel. It is, however, very expensive at the present time, so it is mainly used with glass fibre to reduce costs.

The lamination is formed in the same way as for GRP, only the carbon tows are spaced a little apart on top of the glass matting. It is used to strengthen such things as racing car bodies, archery bows, canoe paddles – all of which have to withstand great strain.

What would the rudder of a boat be made from – GRP or CRP?

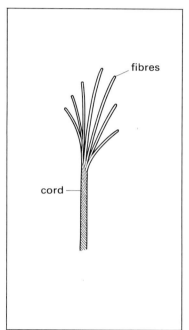

Fig. 3.48

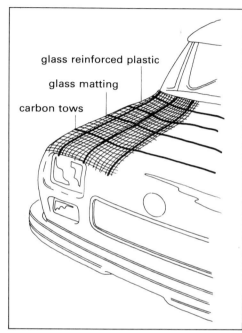

Fig. 3.49

Foams and expanded plastics

These are a widely used form of plastic, and can be thermosetting or thermoplastic. They have a sponge-like appearance. The two main types are: *polyurethane* and *polystyrene*.

Polyurethane foam

This can be either rigid or flexible and is made by cross-linking two compounds and then mixing. The reaction causes carbon dioxide, which expands with the heat that is generated by the process. This results in a honeycomb or cellular structure, something like soap suds only in a more solid form. **Polyester polyurethane** foam has a closed cell structure which makes it rigid and buoyant. **Polyether polyurethane** foam has an open cell structure which makes it flexible and non-buoyant.

It is possible to make up a closed mould and to pour in the foam mixture. The reaction takes place and the foam fills the enclosed space. This method is used a great deal in industry for making foam shapes e.g. chairs, boat hulls, insulation. In schools, however, it is in the ready-made slab or block that polyurethane foam is known.

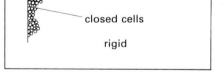

Fig. 3.50   Polyester polyurethane

Which foam would you use to make a life buoy?

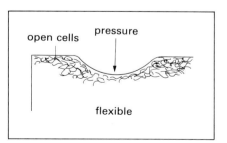

Fig. 3.51   Polyether polyurethane

Shaping plastics

A face mask is needed because
the dust is quite harmful.

Shaping rigid foam is quite easy if you use any of the workshop saws; but a face mask is needed because of the dust which results. If fine detail has to be shaped, a sharp knife or file will work the material. To join pieces together a latex or PVA adhesive bonds without any problems. The foam is an ideal core material for GRP work; boat hulls are made by bonding the GRP around the foam making up a light, yet strong, rigid structure.

Shaping flexible foam is much more difficult, as the material collapses with the weight of most cutting tools. The woodworkers' bandsaw cuts this foam very well, but is limited in the size and type of shaping possible. For intricate work the best tool is an electric knife, but it has to be used with care. A sharp modelling knife can be used successfully on thin sections. It is best to use a contact adhesive for bonding this type of foam; some manufactured adhesives can damage polyurethane so it is wise to try it on scrap material first.

Why do you think a bandsaw cuts
flexible foam, yet a tenon saw
cannot?

Pieces of foam can be joined together with natural latex adhesive.

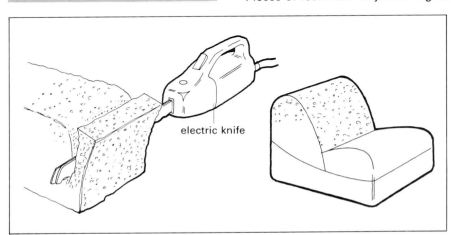

Fig. 3.52

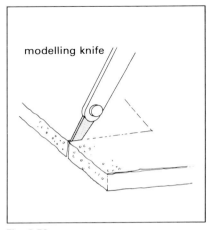

modelling knife

Fig. 3.53

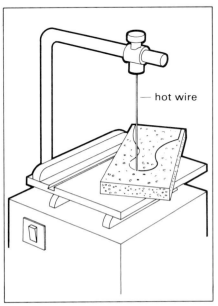

Fig. 3.54   Shaping polystyrene

hot wire

Expanded polystyrene

This is made by adding a volatile hydrocarbon liquid to the polystyrene. This results in the formation of tiny beads. When the beads are heated to 100°C, normally by steam, the hydrocarbon in the mixture vaporises or changes to a gas, which blows up the beads. This can expand the beads by as much as 40 times their original size. To control this, the heating is done in two stages: pre-expanding to a set volume; then placing the beads in shaped moulds before a second expansion takes place. In a confined mould the beads soften with the heat and as they expand fuse together to form a mass of material. By doing this, it is possible to shape the expanded polystyrene into complicated packaging, insulation and advertising design forms.

Shaping polystyrene foam in the workshop is a little different; so it is the ready-formed slabs or blocks that tend to be used. These can be cut to shape with the woodworkers' saw or a sharp modelling knife; but the foam does tend to crumble somewhat if the blades are not sharp.

The best method of shaping is to use a hot wire cutter, which can be hand held (Fig. 3.55) or table model (Fig. 3.54). A low voltage electric current is passed through a piece of nickel/chromium wire, which has a low resistance. The result is that the wire heats up, melting the expanded polystyrene on contact. In this way, complicated shapes and designs can be cut out quickly and easily without any crumbling of the material.

3   Plastics

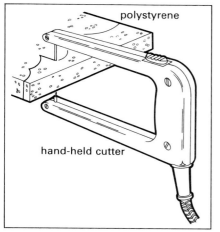

Fig. 3.55

How would you mark out a soft material like expanded polystyrene?

What are the advantages and disadvantages in using expanded polystyrene for our watch stand?

What objects can you think of that come packaged in expanded polystyrene?

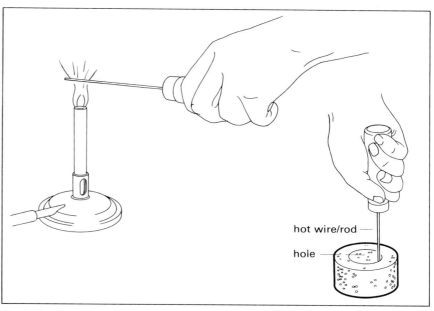

Fig. 3.56

Another simple way of shaping the expanded polystyrene is to heat a piece of wire or thin metal rod with a gas flame. Once hot this can be used to cut in the same way as the electric wire cutter. It is an ideal method for cutting holes or inside shapes, but it does need constant reheating when in use.

S When polystyrene is cut in this way fumes are given off. Keep the room well ventilated.

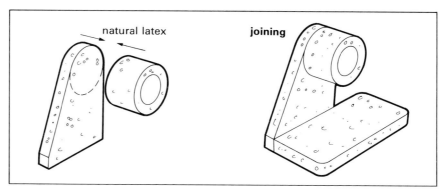

Fig. 3.57

Cutting plastics

It is possible to shape or cut many of the plastics – e.g. nylon, acrylic, polypropylene etc – by using wood and metal cutting tools. The tenon saw, hacksaw, file, plane and twist drill, along with the machine tools such as the lathe, bandsaw, circular saw and milling machine can all be used. The main difference for cutting plastics is that the work must remain cool at all times. If not, the plastic will soften causing the work to distort and discolour; so spoiling the finish.

Cooling

You can use soapy water, soluble oil or paraffin as a cooling liquid. Another method is to use compressed air, which is blown over the surface.

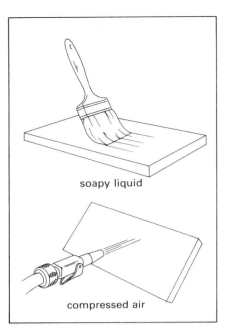

soapy liquid

compressed air

Fig. 3.58

What disadvantage would soapy water have if used on a machine such as a lathe?

Holding plastics

As most of the plastics can mark and bend easily, care is needed to protect the surface and to support them well while working. The surface can be protected by using paper or wood, or when drilling through plastic by using an adhesive tape. The plastic must be held firmly with little chance to flex, and wood may be used to stiffen while working takes place.

Filing and planing

To cut the plastic, it must be held in such a way as to prevent flexing e.g. in a vice or cramped to the bench. It is best to use a low-angled plane, such as a block plane, so that a slicing cut may be taken. A double-cut file will also cut in this manner.

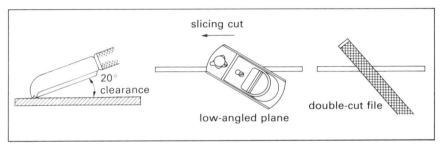

slicing cut

20° clearance

low-angled plane

double-cut file

Fig. 3.59

If wood was not used under plastic sheet when drilling, what would be the result?

Scraping

The woodworkers' cabinet scraper can be used on acrylic sheet to produce an excellent finish.

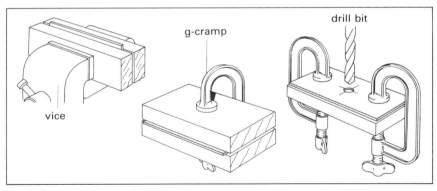

drill bit

g-cramp

vice

Fig. 3.60

Sawing

All the normal wood and metal cutting saws will work with plastics providing they are sharp, but the hacksaw and coping saw are perhaps best. For cutting acrylics the teeth of the saw should be fine, about 14 teeth per 24mm, to prevent chipping. Nylon requires a coarser blade, with 8 teeth per 25mm, with a good set to prevent overheating and clogging. The abra-file is an excellent saw for internal curves and shapes.

Why must acrylic sheet not be allowed to flex while it is being sawn?

3 Plastics

It is wise to drill a release hole in the acrylic sheet when cutting out sections. This is to prevent cracking.

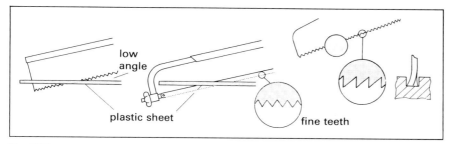

Fig. 3.61

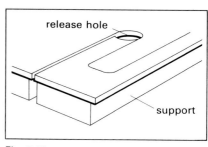

Fig. 3.62

Why do you think it is not wise to use a centre punch on the material first?

Drilling

For drilling plastic, the normal twist drill should be modified to give a slicing action. The tip is re-ground to give a flatter point (Fig. 3.63). This stops the drill from breaking through the material before all of the cutting edge is in contact.

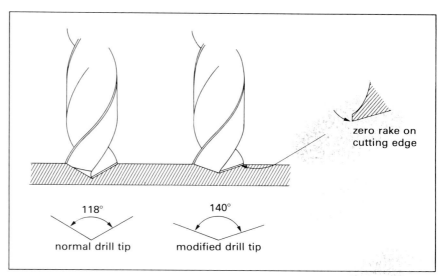

Fig. 3.63

If a drilling machine is being used, the speed of the drill should be quite fast with a very slow feed into the work.

Fig. 3.64

What method would be best for keeping the work cool?

Turning

To produce the slicing action on the lathe, the tool is given 0° rake but a large amount of clearance (15° − 20°). The tip is radiused to prevent digging into the surface and scratching. High speeds can be used for the cutting providing the work and the tool are kept cool.

Threading

It is possible to cut threads on plastic with the normal metalworkers' taps and dies. The coarser types are used, to give as strong a thread as possible. As most thermoplastics give when being cut, then recover, a thread will be slightly incorrect; so adjustments to the die must be made to match the screw and hole.

Shaping plastics

141

Industrial processes

Most of the processes we have discussed for shaping plastic can be used both in schools and in industry. However, it is worthwhile to mention some other processes that are only used in industry – due to the size of equipment required.

Extrusion moulding

Can you think of a kitchen tool that also extrudes material e.g. food?

This is a similar process to injection moulding; thermoplastics are used in granule or powdered form. The granules are put into a hopper, which feeds them into a heated barrel. Inside the barrel is a revolving screw which carries the plastic forward in a continuous flow, once it has become soft.

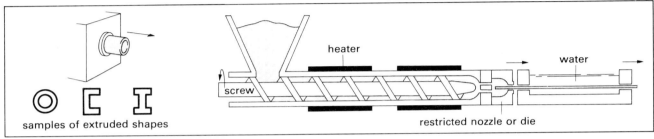

Fig. 3.65   Extrusion machine

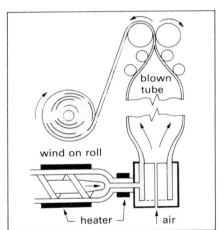

Fig. 3.66   Blow extrusion

Fitted to the end of the barrel is a restricted nozzle or die. As the softened plastic is forced through the die, it takes up the restricted shape. In this way, a continuous stream or extrusion of shaped plastic (tube, rail, angle, rod or sheet), flows from the machine.

On leaving the machine, the material is cooled by water or air. It is then cut into required lengths. Such things as drain and water pipes, curtain rails, sliding door track, double-glazed window sections, are made in this way.

If needed, the hot extruded tube can be used straightaway for blow moulding (see page 130) or it can be blown out, stretching the plastic to make very thin plastic film or foil.

Calendering

This process, like the extruder, has a continuous flow of material leaving the machine. Softened thermoplastic is fed from a hopper between heated

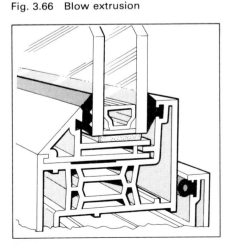

Fig. 3.67

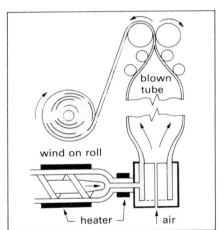

Fig. 3.68   Calendering

What would the plastic film be used for?

What would happen if the sheet was not cooled towards the end of rolling?

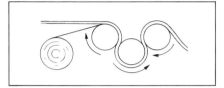

Fig. 3.69

rollers. These rollers squeeze the plastic into a sheet form; starting thick in section but becoming thinner as it passes between further rollers. The rollers are graded in temperature; colder the further along the machine they are. The rollers cool and compress the sheet even more. The last two rollers control the final thickness of the sheet plastic. This is determined by the distance they are set apart.

If a pattern is cut into the final rollers, they will impart this design to the passing sheet. Film or sheet can be produced in large quantities, for use as packaging, damp-proofing, roofing material or display signs.

A further extension to the process, is to add another roller containing a backing material such as paper or cloth. This is squeezed together with the hot plastic: a bond is formed, giving a coated material such as vinyl wallpaper. Such material has the advantage of being able to withstand damp conditions or is washable on the outer surface, yet the inner paper surface can be glued to the wall easily.

Rotational moulding

This process is used to produce single items that are hollow, such as dustbins and road cones. A measured amount of thermoplastic (polythene) is fed into a light, drum-shaped mould. This is spun slowly in two different directions, as the mould heats up. The softened plastic flows all over the inner drum shape as the mould spins. When the spinning motion stops the mould is allowed to cool. Once cool, the moulded shape can be removed.

How do the spinning forces make the plastic take up the mould shape?

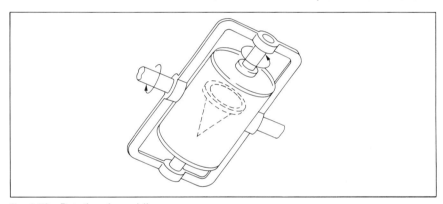

Fig. 3.70   Rotational moulding

3.6 JOINING PLASTICS

Many designs are built up from a number of pieces of material; these may be similar or involve the use of other plastics or they may be wood or metal.

Temporary fastenings

These are used when the pieces or parts have to be taken apart for use or maintenance.

Plastic push fits

These use the principle that many plastics are flexible and will move to a small degree without breaking. The work is designed with the joint as part of

What other things can you think of which use this system?

the overall object, so that when the two pieces are together they form one unit. One part of the joint acts as the locking system, the other as the flexible link. As the two are pushed together they flex and lock, and by squeezing them the joint can be broken. In this way, pieces can be joined and unjoined quickly without having to use any other pieces. The joint is simple and clean but is limited because it will not stand great pressure.

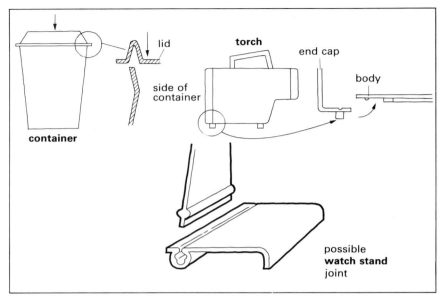

Fig. 3.71   Plastic push fits

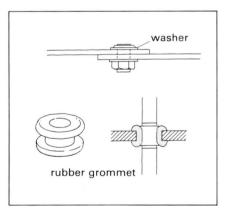

Fig. 3.72

When threading nylon a larger tapping drill is needed. Why will a normal drill not work?

Why do you think staples are used for upholstery in place of nails?

Screws and grommets

Screws may be used for joining plastics to themselves and to many other materials, including wood and metal. It is important that the plastic surface is protected by means of washers to help spread the pressure. Holes should have rubber grommets fitted to allow for any expansion or movement that could damage the plastic. Many of the plastics can be threaded in a similar way to metals so that the work itself contains the screw.

Permanent fastenings

Nails and staples

These may sometimes be used for joining certain plastics to other materials, when they are produced in film, sheet or fabric form. Such plastics as PVC,

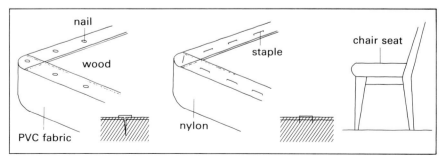

Fig. 3.73   Nails and staples for fastening

nylon and polyethylene are often held in this way. The system is limited as most plastics will tear under strain, or the rigid plastics will crack and break up.

Solvent bonding

This is used to join similar plastics, by using a suitable solvent to soften the joining edges so that they can fuse together. As the solvent evaporates the joint re-hardens to form a very good bond. For the join to be successful, the two pieces must be as close fitting as possible. Masking tape is placed around the joint area, making sure that only the relevant faces are affected. The faces are first cleaned with an abrasive paper or a cleaning fluid such as trichloro-ethane. The edges can then be dipped in solvent or it can be applied with a squeeze dropper. The joints are limited in strength and can deteriorate in damp conditions.

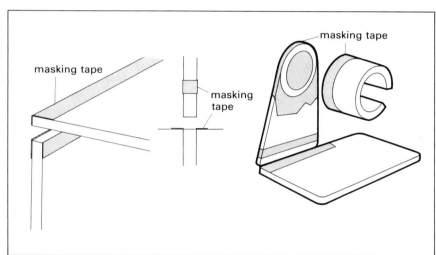

Fig. 3.74

Typical solvents

Plastic	Solvent
ABS	Methylene chloride
Acrylic	Ethylene dichloride
Nylon	Aqueous phenol
Polystyrene	Methylene chloride

Table 12

Some plastics, such as polyethylene, polypropylene and PTFE, do not have suitable solvents and so cannot be joined in this way.

Cements

These are solvents with a small amount of the same plastic ready mixed together to form a rubber dough-type cement. It is used in tube or gun form for spreading. The cement can fill gaps and gives a very strong, weatherproof bond.

Care has to be taken with some of the solvents, as fumes are given off. The room must be well ventilated and a face mask should be worn.

Why should masking tape be so important to a good joint?

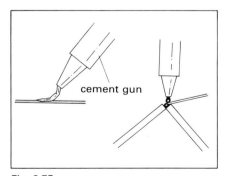

Fig. 3.75

Why would a rigid type adhesive be of little use for foams?

Adhesives

These can be used for almost all plastics. There is a wide range available. The adhesive will vary according to what plastic is being joined and whether the materials are similar. Most manufacturers state what can and what cannot be bonded with their product. The three adhesives listed in Table 13 will cover most materials.

Adhesive	Trade name	Instructions	Uses
Epoxy resin	Araldite (2 pack: resin and hardener)	Mix resin and hardener; will harden in 24 hours	Bonds most plastics, including polythene; expensive – limited to small joint work
Impact	Evostik (rubber based; ready mixed)	Spread over both joint surfaces; leave to let solvent evaporate; place 2 surfaces together. Bond is instant.	Most plastics, but can stain and wrinkle PVC and cause expanded polystyrene to dissolve
Natural latex	Copydex (rubber, ready mixed)	Quick drying and forms strong but flexible bond that is waterproof	Ideal for most foam type plastics

Table 13

Welding

It is possible to melt two similar pieces of thermoplastic, so that they can flow and join together; the main exception being PTFE, which only decomposes on softening. The way the plastics are heated can vary, but the three most common methods are:

Friction welding – used a great deal for joining rigid thermoplastics, such as nylon, acrylic, PVC. The materials have to be similar for the joint to work, as they must both melt at the same time. This method works on the principle that if two surfaces are rubbed together quickly enough they will create friction and heat. If this heat is great enough it will soften the material and they can bond.

If a circular piece of material is set up in the lathe or drill, spun at great speed and then brought into contact with another piece of material, friction will take place. The material will soften in 1–2 seconds. The spinning is stopped but the parts are kept under pressure contact. The weld forms and the material cools and hardens.

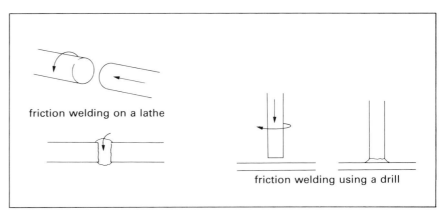

friction welding on a lathe

friction welding using a drill

Fig. 3.76

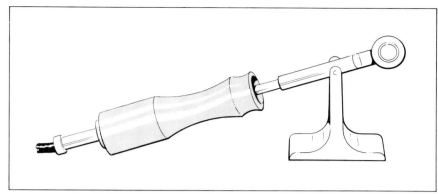

Fig. 3.77 Hot tool welder

Why do you think hot tool welding is of little use on thick materials?

Why should hot air be used to soften the plastic and not a naked flame?

Hot tool welding – uses a heated tool, similar to an electrical soldering iron, only the end has a knurled roller in place of a pointed tip. It works by drawing the tool over the two clamped pieces of work. The system is mainly used for joining thin film or sheet material.

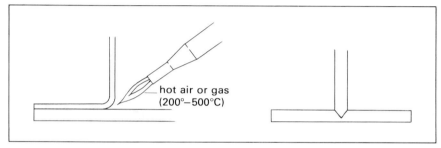

Fig. 3.78 Hot gas welding

Hot gas welding – uses a filler rod of the same material to join the work together. The plastic edges to be joined are heated with hot air or nitrogen, using a small electrical torch. As they soften, the filler rod is added. This in turn softens and they all bond together. The torch is slowly moved backwards over the joint until the weld is completed. On cooling, the joint is as strong as the original material. To allow for the rod or extra material, the joint area is always prepared first, by cleaning and cutting bevels or spaces. This method is used for joining most of the thermoplastics: PVC, acrylic, polyethylene, polypropylene, ABS.

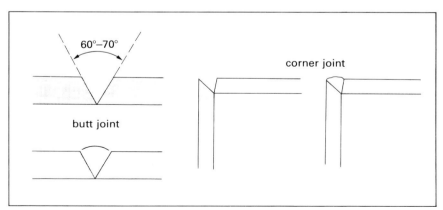

Fig. 3.79

Joining plastics

Dip coating

This is, as its title suggests, a method of using plastics as a coating material on metal surfaces – to provide protection, colour and safe handling. Thermoplastics are used (e.g. polythene, polyvinyl chloride, cellulose acetate and nylon). They are all used in a powdered form, which is contained in a fluidising tank. This is a large box or drum that has a compressed air inlet at the bottom; set above this is a porous base which spreads the air in an even mass. As the compressed air is turned on, it passes through the powder separating the tiny particles, making them float and act as if they had become a fluid.

Why will the coated object need some form of support when it is returned to the oven?

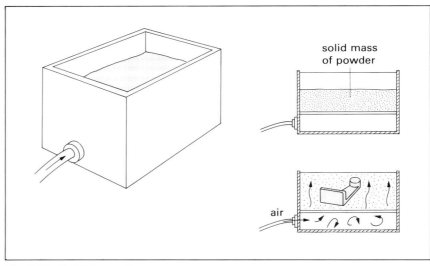

Fig. 3.80   Fluidising tank

The metal to be coated is first cleaned and degreased, or the plastic will not hold to the surface. It is then placed in an oven and heated to about 180°C (depending on the thickness of the metal object). The hot metal is removed from the oven, using tongs or holding wires. The hot metal is dipped into the fluidised powder for a few seconds and then removed and shaken. What has happened is that the powder has floated all around the object, and as it comes into contact with the surface it has melted and formed a coating. Once the surface is covered the metal is removed and surplus powder is shaken off.

The metal object is returned to the oven and reheated to fuse the coat evenly. It can then be removed and allowed to cool.

This system of coating is used on milk crates, refrigerator baskets and shelves, dish drainers, vegetable racks, flower baskets (polythene); tool handles, electrical fittings (PVC): door handles and knobs, coat hooks, hand rails (cellulose acetate butyrate); and artificial limb appliances for disabled people (nylon).

Plastic coated tray

4.1 GROWTH AND STRUCTURE

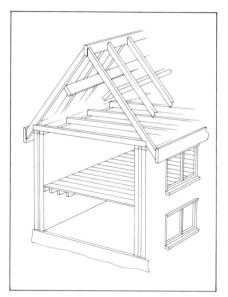

Fig. 4.1   Timber used in a house

Can you list 10 items around the house that are made from wood?

What do you think would happen to the tree if a ring of bark was removed from it?

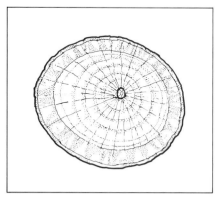

Fig. 4.3   Four-year-old lime tree

What would a large amount of growth on an annual ring suggest?

Wood is one of the oldest raw materials known, yet it continues to play a major role in modern-day life. It is used in such things as furniture, housing, toys and newspapers.

Before going on to discuss wood as a design material we need to look at its source: the tree. There are well over 2000 different varieties of tree and they grow in most parts of the world – from the cold climates of the north to the tropical climates of the equator. The tree also provides us with fruit, nuts, oil, cork, flowers, colours, scents etc. It has one other important feature that is very important to the human race: it absorbs carbon dioxide and gives out oxygen. It is, however, the many different coloured, textured and strength woods that we obtain from the tree that concern us more in design and technology.

How a tree grows

Like any plant, the tree derives its food from the soil in which it grows; taking up water and mineral salts with its roots. The food travels up the tree, in the form of crude sap, by what is called the sapwood of the tree. On reaching the leaves, the natural sunlight and carbon dioxide absorbed from the atmosphere, convert the sap or food into sugar and starches. Once the crude sap is converted to **elaborated sap**, it travels down the tree. It does this just under the bark, by what is called the **bast**. As it does this, it forms new wood cells – called the **cambium layer** – which divide into softwood cells on the inside and bast cells on the outside.

Some food is taken into the inner part of the tree by means of little passageways, called **medullary rays**. This helps to convert the sapwood into a more solid form called **heartwood**.

It is this mature part of the tree that provides the most usable wood or timber, because it is harder and stronger than the newly-formed sapwood. As the tree grows in size, more and more of the heartwood is formed.

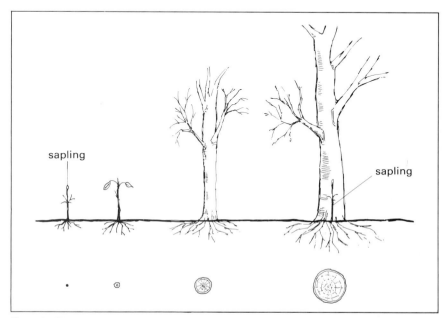

sapling

sapling

Fig. 4.2   Tree growth

Growth and structure

Coniferous tree – Norway spruce

The growing process starts each spring, when the growth is very quick and a great deal of new sapwood is formed. This slows down in the summer and autumn to a smaller, denser amount of sapwood. This growing process is seen clearly in the leaves: the bright green leaves of spring produce a lot of food; the duller leaves of summer, followed by the brown and red of autumn, producing little food; until the leaves fall and growing stops, with the coming of winter.

So each year a new band of wood forms around the tree, made up of spring and summer/autumn growth. This is called the **annual ring**. From this it is possible to tell the age of a tree, and what each year's growth was like. For example, if it was a very dry year the tree will have had little food, so the growth will be quite small. It should be remembered that trees from tropical climates will have little check on their growth, so the annual rings are less clearly defined.

Types of trees

Trees fall into two broad categories: *softwoods* (coniferous) and *hardwoods* (deciduous).

Type of tree	Description	Wood	Problems
Softwood (coniferous)	Evergreen: with needle type leaves (e.g. the pine)	Normally light, soft, easily worked	Great many knots and large amount of resin
Hardwood (deciduous)	Non-evergreen, broad-leaved (e.g. oak, ash)	Slower growing so much denser and harder wood; wider range of colours – from black to red	Few knots, but are difficult to work

Table 14

Why do you think hardwoods are used for more decorative type work?

Some trees fail to fit into these guidelines; for example, pitch pine which can be called a softwood is very hard and strong; while balsa is classed as a hardwood but is quite soft and weak. The only true method of distinction between a hardwood and a softwood, is to look at the wood fibres or cell structure of a sample.

The structure of wood

Softwood structure

Softwood is made up of millions of tiny cells; the main type being called a **tracheid**. These are like thin tubes which are sealed at the ends and have small holes in the tube surface.

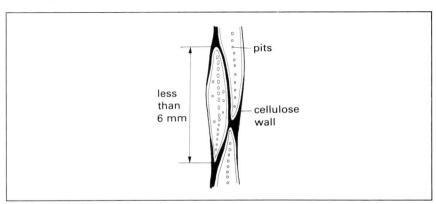

Fig. 4.4   Softwood

Deciduous tree – sessile oak

Why do you think that, in Fig. 4.5, (a) will work well when cut, yet (b) will tear?

These cells build together in the direction of growth, to form the structure of the tree and carry the crude sap from the roots to the leaves. We see this as the **grain** of the wood e.g. the direction of the cells as they lie together. Sometimes between the cells are little pockets of food or resin, brought by the medullary rays and stored.

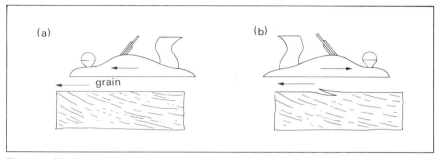

Fig. 4.5   Planing

Hardwood structure

Hardwoods are made up of two main types of cells: fibres and pores or vessels. Fibres are small cells, long and narrow in shape but with very thick cell walls. These are what give the tree its hardness and strength; but they do not carry any crude sap like the softwood tracheid. **Pores or vessels** are cells which act as little pipes. They are built on top of each other to carry the food for the tree. They appear in hardwoods in two different forms:

1. as an evenly spread system of pores throughout the tree. These can be seen in such woods as beech and birch. This is called *diffuse porous* wood and gives a smooth surface to the wood.

2. as a system of different size rings of pores around the tree, called *ring porous* wood. It can be seen in such woods as oak, elm, ash. It gives a much coarser surface.

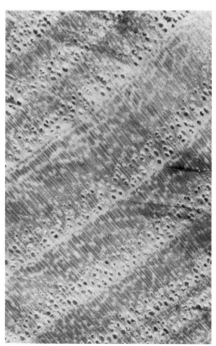

Fig. 4.6   Hardwood

Why do you think it is much easier to drive a nail into softwood than hardwood?

Tree	Places grown	Wood colour
Common hardwoods Oak	British Isles, Europe, USA, Japan	Several species: English – light yellow-brown, with silver grain Japanese – light brown, tinged with grey
Beech	Europe, British Isles	White to pale brown
Mahogany	Central & South America, West Indies, West Africa	Several varieties: pink to reddish-brown
Walnut	Europe, Africa, USA, Japan, Australia	Several varieties: mid-brown with dark stripes English – black stripe Australian – dark brown stripe European – pinkish stripe
Teak	India, Burma	Golden brown
Obeche	Congo	White to pale straw
Balsa	Central & South America	Light straw
Common softwoods European redwood (Scots, Pine, Red Deal)	British Isles, Scandinavia, Russia	Pale to reddish-brown
Sitka Spruce (Whitewood)	British Isles, Europe, USA, Canada	Cream to light golden yellow, brown
Parana Pine	South America	Pale cream to brown with purple
Western Red Cedar	Canada	Reddish-brown with strong odour
Douglas Fir (Oregon Pine, Columbian Pine)	Canada, USA	Gold to reddish-brown

Table 15

Properties	Uses
English – very strong, tough, durable Japanese – less strong but even-textured; can be worked quite easily	Furniture, veneers, panelling; doors, windows, roofs, gates, fencing
Close grain that works and finishes well; hard and strong; but not durable outdoors	Functional furniture; toys; tools; turned ware
African (e.g. Gaboon, Sapele, Utile) – quite hard and strong; but not easy to finish American – easier to work; gives high finish	Indoor work only – furniture, panelling, veneers, pattern making
All highly decorative; vary according to variety. Australian – soft and close grain. English – hard, tough; difficult to obtain. African – low in weight and strength	Superior joinery – furniture, veneers, floor blocks
Natural oils make it very durable; hard, strong and fire resistant; works well but quickly blunts tools	Fine furniture – chairs, tables, etc.; superior joinery – door, windows, shop fronts, boat building
Very light and soft timber, easily worked; coarse texture; not very durable	General indoor work (often hidden and painted) – framework, drawers
Very light and soft, yet strong for its weight	Model making; rafts, lifebelts, refrigerators
Quite strong and hard, with straight grain; works well, but impaired by knots; very durable when preserved	General woodwork – doors, cupboards, shelves etc.; building – roofs, floors etc.
Tough but easily worked; straight grain; contains resin pockets but resists splitting	Indoor work only – low cost furniture, steps, flooring, packing cases
Tough with fine grain; shrinks rapidly on drying; also prone to twisting	General indoor workwork – shelves, cupboards, fitted furniture
Straight grain; soft and weak; works well with sharp tools; natural oils make it outstandingly durable against weather, insects and rot	Decorative and protective – panelling, weather boarding, linen chests
Strong, with straight grain; slightly resinous; quite durable but needs protection if used outdoors	Furniture; plywood; door, windows, frames

Table 15

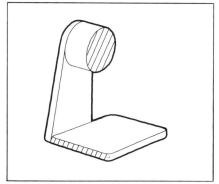

Fig. 4.7

Once again the list of possible materials that could be used for our watch stand is large.

oak – very strong and tough, with interesting colour and grain;
mahogany – hard and strong, with excellent finish;
redwood – very light yet strong.

Hardwoods and softwoods

153

Conversion of timber

When the tree is fully grown, it will have the maximum amount of heartwood and is ready to be felled. If left, the tree will start to decay from the centre and will continue to do so until it dies or is blown down.

The tree is best felled in winter, when it contains little sap and moisture. (Excess sap can cause shrinkage problems with newly-cut timber). Once felled, the tree has its branches removed, and the trunk is cut into reasonable size *logs*. The bark is then removed from the logs and it is ready for cutting up into usable shapes and sizes of wood. This is called *conversion*.

The way the logs can be cut up varies according to the type of wood and whether it has special features. For example, a wood may have a grain or figure that only shows up well when it is cut in a certain direction. However, some methods do waste great amounts of wood; so cost does play a major part in the final method used.

Why are many saw mills set beside rivers?

Slab cutting (through and through)

This is the simplest and cheapest method of converting the log. Parallel slices or slabs are cut through the wood (Fig. 4.8). It does not waste any material and gives very wide boards. The problem is that as the wood dries it shrinks unevenly and tends to warp badly. It is a method that is mainly used for the cheaper forms of softwood.

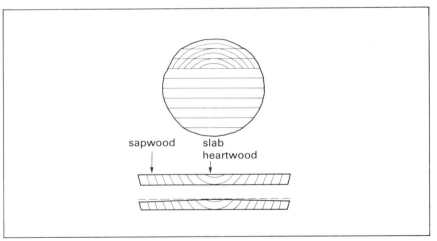

sapwood   slab
           heartwood

Fig. 4.8   Slab cutting

Tangential cutting

This is used on trees with very distinct annual rings that show up well when cut, e.g. pitch pine. The cuts are made at a tangent to the annual rings, thus getting the best grain effect (Fig. 4.9). Woods cut like this may twist or warp, if not held down when used.

Why will sapwood shrink more than heartwood?

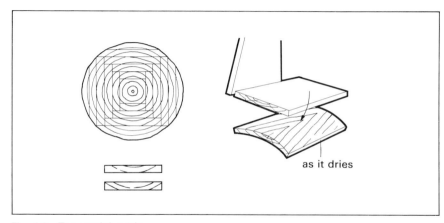

Fig. 4.9   Tangential cutting

Radial cutting (quarter sawn)

This is the most expensive way of converting timber, as it wastes considerable amounts of material. The log is first cut into quarters; and then cut on radial lines from the centre (Fig. 4.10). The idea is to get the annual rings as near to 90° to the cut board as possible. In this way the shrinkage is reduced, so the wood has less tendency to twist or warp. This method is used on *oak*, as it shows up the medullary rays of the wood in the form of silver grain.

Less wasteful methods of converting the radially cut quarter can be used, but the shrinkage problems start to increase when the annual rings are not at 90°.

The cut timber is not ready for use, as it still contains a great amount of moisture. If used in this state it would be very heavy, difficult to work and liable to decay; and on drying out it would shrink and crack. The wood has to

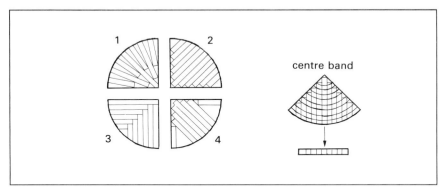

Fig. 4.10   Radial cutting

Timber shrinks most along the line of the annual rings. Is this true or false? And why?

be dried out or seasoned, until it contains just the right amount of moisture for the atmosphere in which it is to be used. For example, if the wood is to be used out of doors its moisture content should be about 16%, but if it is used in a normally heated house it should have about 11–13%.

Seasoning

The drying out of the cut timber can be carried out in one of two ways: *natural* or *kiln seasoning*.

Natural seasoning

In this method the cut boards or planks are stacked on a flat piece of ground which is covered with concrete or ashes. This is to keep the ground free from weeds and to stop any form of decay developing. The boards are separated from each other by means of sticks. This is to allow air to circulate round the timber. A roof or shelter is normally put over the wood to stop the rain and sun from spoiling the gradual seasoning process. This method is slow – a piece of 25mm board will take about a year to reduce its moisture content to a usable level.

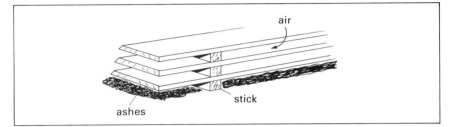

Fig. 4.11

Kiln seasoning

As time is very important and it is expensive to leave wood unused for long periods, a quicker method of drying has to be used in some circumstances. The boards are stacked on trolleys, separated by sticks. The trolleys are run into large ovens or kilns and the wood is subjected to heat and steam sprays. The moisture content can be reduced quickly and accurately, to below those obtained by natural methods in a matter of weeks.

This method also allows an exact moisture content to be given to a wood for a special situation, by taking samples of the wood during the drying. Many craftworkers, however, dispute the quality of timber produced in this way and state that it loses its colour and feel.

Why should kiln seasoning be an expensive method of treating wood?

The current available forms and sizes of timber

Timber is marketed in three main ways:

rough sawn timber – which is the nominal or full size;

ready machined – planed on both sides (**PBS**) – which is approximately 3mm smaller in thickness;

ready machined – planed all round (**PAR**) – which is approximately 3mm smaller in width and thickness.

Boards

These are timber that is 100mm or more wide, and under 50mm thick.

in *hardwoods* – lengths are mainly 1.8 metres and above;
widths are mainly 150mm to 300mm.

in *softwoods* – lengths are mainly 1.8 metres and above;
widths are mainly 100mm to 200mm.

PBS to sizes shown – 9, 12, 16, 19, 22mm thick.

Boards are sold by the square metre, so to find the amount of timber required simply multiply the board *length* in metres by the board *width* in millimetres and divide by 1000.

$$\text{Board length (m)} \times \frac{\text{board width (mm)}}{1000} = \text{Area in square metres}$$

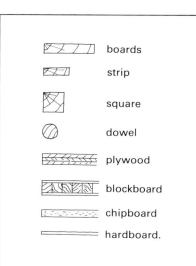

boards

strip

square

dowel

plywood

blockboard

chipboard

hardboard.

Fig. 4.12

Therefore a board 4 metres long and 100mm wide would be as follows:

$$4 \times \frac{100}{1000} = 0.4m^2$$

Strips

This is timber that is under 100mm wide and under 50mm thick. Lengths are mainly 1.5 metres and up.
PAR – to sizes shown: 22 x 35, 22 x 47, 22 x 72mm.

Squares

This is square section timber with sides 25mm and over. Lengths are mainly 1.0 metres and up.
PAR – to sizes shown: 22 x 22, 35 x 35, 47 x 47mm.
  Both strips and squares are sold by length or lineal metre.

Dowel

This is round section timber that is from 4 to 38mm in diameter. Lengths are mainly 0.9m to 2.4m.
ϕ 4, 6, 8, 9, 12, 15, 18, 21, 25, 28, 34, 38mm.

Plywood

There are many different grades but sheet sizes are as follows: 1500 x 1500mm, 1220 x 2440mm.
Thickness: 1.5, 3, 4, 6, 9, 12, 15, 18mm.

Blockboard and laminboard

Again a range of grades are available but sheet sizes are: 1220 x 2440mm.
Thickness: 12, 16, 19, 22, 24, 32mm.

Chipboard

Once again a small range of grades; sheet size – 1220 x 2440mm.
Thickness: 9, 12, 18mm.

Hardboard

Different grades, sizes: 1220 x 2440mm with thicknesses 3.2, 4.8, 6.0mm.

4.4 DEFECTS AND DISEASES

Before using a piece of seasoned wood, care must be taken to check it for defects and faults. These may have occurred in the wood during its growth or during seasoning. If this check is not done, a piece of work may be spoilt by the fault showing up at a much later stage.

Common faults or defects

Knots

These are the remains of the tree branches and can weaken the wood by causing sharp changes in the direction of the grain. They also make the wood more difficult to work, because of their hardness and change of grain direction. Knots can be in two forms:

Live – firm and embedded in place, leaving the wood quite strong but difficult to work.

Dead – loose and will eventually fall out of place, and greatly weaken the wood.

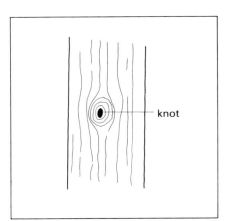

Fig. 4.13

What timber will have more knots, hardwood or softwood? Why?

Shakes

This can be any form of split or crack, and usually takes its name from the pattern they form. They may start small but will get larger as the wood dries out and so will spoil and weaken that piece.

Cup shake – split formed round an annular ring, so that a loose section starts to lift out of place.

Thunder shake – crack across the grain, caused by bad felling. Any strain on the wood at this point will cause it to break.

End checks – splits on the ends of boards caused by unequal drying. This means that large amounts of wood are wasted by having to cut out the split section.

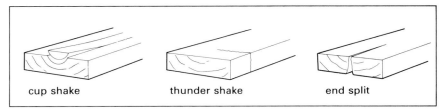

cup shake   thunder shake   end split

Fig. 4.14

Resin pockets

These are small cavities full of resin or surplus food. They can be a source of weakness. The main problem is that the resin starts to flow or weep long after cutting, and can spoil a piece of work by affecting the final finish.

Cupping or bowing

This is caused by bad stacking when the timber was being seasoned, allowing the wood to cup or curl in the direction of the annual rings. Bowing is due to bad support in the length of the board, allowing it to sag. The bowed board needs to be cut out.

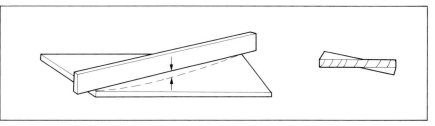

Fig. 4.15   Twisting

4 Wood

How could you check a piece of wood to see if it was twisted?

Twisting

This is another seasoning fault and is caused by the board not being weighted down, allowing it to twist in its length. If used, the wood can distort a whole piece of work.

Common diseases and pests

Most new timber will be free from any form of disease, but they may contain a hidden pest – an insect which leaves its telltale tiny holes in the wood surface. The designer must be aware of diseases that can affect wood in certain situations and take precautions to stop them from developing.

Dry rot

This is a sponge-like fungus that feeds on the wood cells. It is highly infectious and can spread very quickly once the growth has started. It is caused by using poorly-seasoned wood fixed in a position that is warm, damp and badly-ventilated: for example, a wall cupboard in an old damp house. Any infected wood becomes very brittle and powdery, hence the name *dry rot*. All infected timber has to be burnt and even the surrounding walls need to be heated with a blow torch for safety.

To prevent this, these precautions should be taken: only use the best quality wood, keep it well ventilated and coat the wood with a water-soluble preservative.

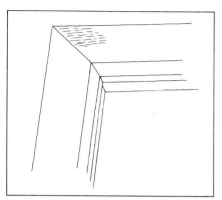

Fig. 4.16   Dry rot

Wood floors are prone to dry rot. Why should this be?

Wet rot

This is also a fungus. It results from the wood being subjected to continuous dampness. The wood becomes dark brown and spongey, and on drying becomes very brittle and weak. It is far more common than dry rot, attacking any outdoor woods that are unprotected, e.g. gates, doors, windows etc. To protect the wood, treat it with a water-repellent preservative, or paint well.

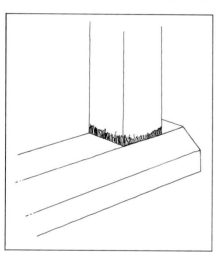

Fig. 4.17   Wet rot

Pests

The insect that causes most damage to wood is the beetle, in its larva or grub state. The **furniture beetle** is the main pest, as it can attack any timber that is unprotected, both new and old, hardwood and softwood. The damage is done by the small white grub or *woodworm*, feeding on the wood. The grub hatches out from eggs laid by the female beetle in a crack or crevice. As the grubs eat away the wood they form tunnels and holes, and so start to weaken the timber. A telltale sign is the fine powder that falls from tiny holes in the wood. The beetle will lay its eggs on any woodwork, not just furniture. All infected timber should be cut out and burnt. Once the larva has matured, it turns into a pupa, before finally emerging as a fully-grown beetle. The precautions to take are: to apply a woodworm insecticide or fluid, fill all cracks or gaps, and, if furniture, apply an insecticide polish.

The **powder post beetle** is a less common pest and tends to be found in woodyards, where it attacks the sapwood of ring porous trees, e.g. oak, ash, elm. It lays eggs into pores of the wood; the grubs then hatch and eat the sapwood. The attack usually dies out with seasoning. The **deathwatch beetle** is a much larger beetle. It tends to attack old oak that has become damp or diseased. For this reason, it is mainly confined to old buildings – church and manor-house roofs. The lifecycle is similar to the furniture beetle, and again it can reduce thick timbers to mere shells. Treatment is the same as for furniture beetle.

The holes in the wood are called flight holes. Why should this be?

4.5 MANUFACTURED BOARDS

The tree limits the size of board that can be obtained from its trunk. If it was possible to cut a very wide board, it would tend to shrink and curl, due to the different sections of heartwood and softwood. To overcome this problem and to extend the size and range of work possible, different ways have been developed to reduce wood to another form and then rejoin it in large sheets.

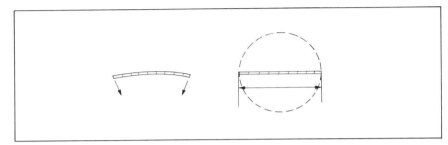

Fig. 4.18

Veneers

These are thin slices of wood that can be used in a sandwich form to make plywood or as a thin decorative layer on a less attractive base. They can be produced in two ways:

Knife cut – the log is cut to a square shape or baulk. It is boiled and steamed to soften the wood structure. Then it is fixed to a sliding table and moved against a knife edge. A thin slice is removed; the table is raised and again moved against the knife edge. This continues until the baulk is cut up. This is an expensive method, but the veneers obtained are very attractive. The veneers are used mainly for matching decoration on another surface.

Rotary cut – uses the log, steamed for easy cutting, mounted on revolving centres. A knife is fed onto the surface, and a continuous stream of veneer peels from the log. As the cut follows the annual rings, the veneer lacks any interest and is only used for general plywood construction.

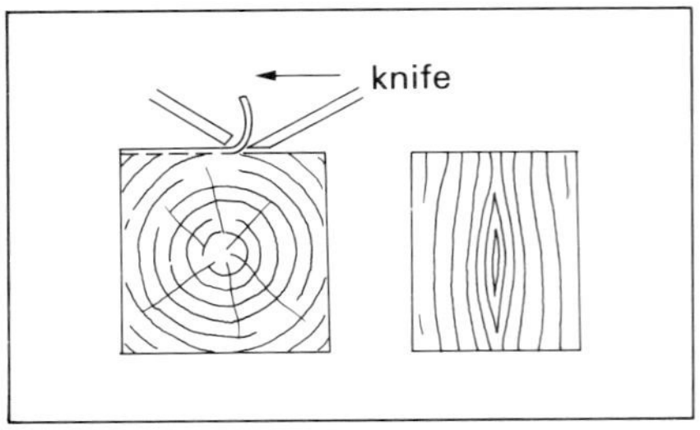

Fig. 4.19 Knife cut

Why should knots present a problem when making veneers?

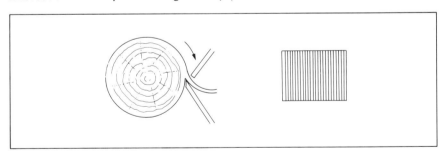

Fig. 4.20 Rotary cut

Plywood

By glueing the thin veneers together with the wood grain of each separate piece at right angles to each other, a very strong material can be formed. The sandwich of veneers is always made in sets of odd numbers – 3, 5, 7, 9 etc. – to counteract the shrinkage of the layers. This means that a flat stable sheet material can be produced in very large sizes. Sometimes one of the outer layers or plys is of a decorative wood such as teak or oak. If the plywood is to be used outdoors, a special waterproof adhesive has to be used to bond the veneers together. It is then said to be water and boil proof (WBP). Interior plywood is usually joined with casein or animal glue.

What kind of things would you expect to see made from ply-wood?

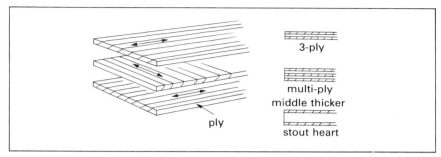

Fig. 4.21

Laminboard

Why do you think the edges of laminboard will need to have facing pieces added if used in furniture making?

When thicker boards are needed, for such things as doors and table tops, it becomes very expensive to build up the many layers of plywood. As a substitute, solid strips of wood are used as the middle of the sandwich, with a veneer on the outer faces. The strips are never more than 7mm wide, and are glued together as well as to the outer veneers. The outer surface can also be used as a base for a decorative veneer when it is used in furniture making.

Blockboard

This is a less expensive method, using much wider strips of wood – about 25mm – as the middle core. It gives a very strong board, but tends to be a little less stable in keeping flat. Care also has to be taken when handling the sheet material as the edges can easily be damaged.

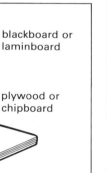

Fig. 4.23 Manufactured board watch stand

blackboard or laminboard

plywood or chipboard

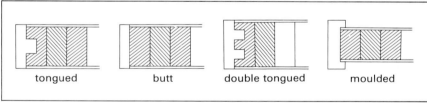

tongued   butt   double tongued   moulded

Fig. 4.22 Lippings for edges of boards

Chipboard

This material is made up of fine particles of wood or chips, which have been compressed together and bonded by a synthetic resin adhesive. By using this method, a very large sheet can be produced at low cost which is quite strong and stable. It can be used as a base and then veneered or given a plastic coating. If it is used in a position where it will be under strain it must be well supported or it will break. It is used a great deal for mass-produced furniture. It is easily damaged.

Why do you think chipboard soon dulls the blade of a cutting tool?

Hardboard

To make this type of boarding, wood pulp is used in place of veneers or chips. The wood pulp is mixed with resin and heated, then compressed into a flat sheet. Boards produced in this way are quite thin, very light and much less expensive than plywood. It does, however, only have one smooth

Manufactured boards

Why must hardboard not be used for external use?

surface; the other surface is textured. This face can be covered with a veneer or plastic. Hardboard is used mainly for covering large areas or spaces where it will not be subjected to any strain, as it is quite weak and needs to be well supported.

Manufactured boards have an important part to play alongside solid wood, and should be used by the designer not as a cheap substitute but as a material of real value. They do present their own problems of working e.g. sawing, planing, chiselling. Joining boards together can also be more difficult; special joints and joining systems have to be used.

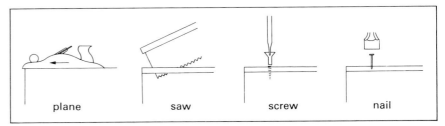

Fig. 4.24

4.6 SHAPING WOODS – CUTTING, TURNING, LAMINATION, BENDING

Cutting wood

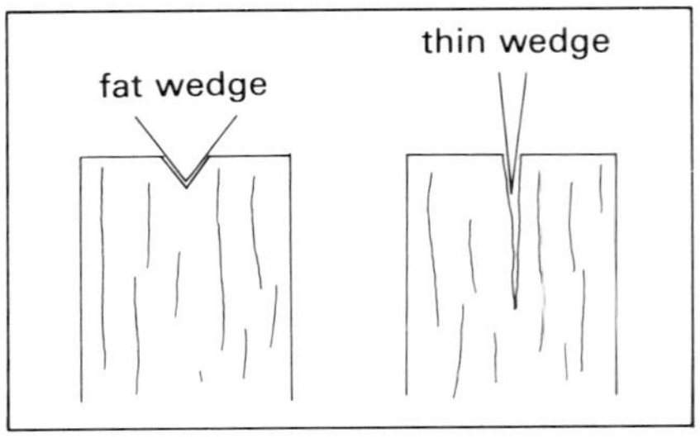

The major method used to shape wood is the removal of unwanted areas by cutting. This may be to obtain the design shape or to produce a joint which, when put together, forms the shape. Any tool that has to cut wood must have a wedge-shaped tip to split or part the fibres of the wood. The thinner the wedge the better the cutting action, but the weaker the tool becomes. So any tool that has to cut softwood and hardwood has to be a compromise.

Chisels

The chisel is a good example of the compromise in the cutting action. It is ground to give the blade tip a thin wedge shape, but is then sharpened or

Fig. 4.25

Why should a fat wedge shape require greater effort when used?

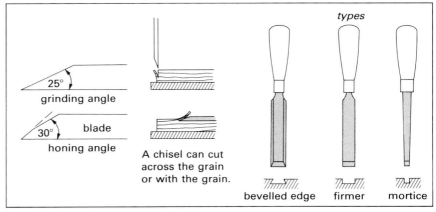

Fig. 4.26 Chisels

honed to give a strong cutting edge. Chisels are made in different cross-sectional shapes, so that they can be used for trimming, paring and joint-making. It is the skill of the user that determines the amount of wood cut each time.

Gouges

These are curved chisels and cut in a similar way to normal chisels. Only two types are made: the **firmer** or outside ground gouge used for cutting hollows or grooves; and the **paring** or inside ground gouge used for trimming curves.

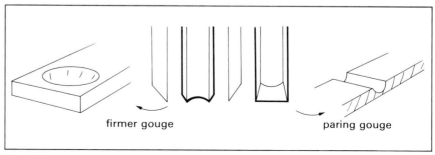

firmer gouge   paring gouge

Fig. 4.27

Planes

When large areas of wood have to be cut a much more controlled system has to be used. This is the plane. It works by having a cutting blade set at an acute angle in a wood or metal body. The blade is sharpened like the chisel, but normally has another plate or backing iron clamped to it to control the amount of splitting that can take place.

How does the mouth or gap in the bottom of a plane also help to control the cut?

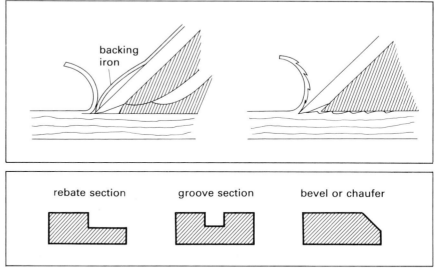

backing iron

rebate section   groove section   bevel or chaufer

Fig. 4.28

The range of different types of plane is large – from simple straight cutting (*smoothing plane*) to ones that will cut grooves or rebates (*plough* and *rebate planes*).

Some of the smaller planes have their blades set round in a similar way to the chisel, but are only used for trimming edges or joints. With these planes, no backing iron is used.

Saws

The saw cuts with wedge-shaped teeth on a thin flexible blade. The direction the saw has to cut the wood affects the design of the teeth. When it is used mainly for cutting with the grain or ripping, the teeth are shaped like small chisels to split the wood quickly. For cutting across the grain or cross cutting, the teeth have a knife-like shape to first cut into the fibres and then remove them. If the cross-cut teeth did not have this shape the wood would split in an uncontrolled way, spoiling the work.

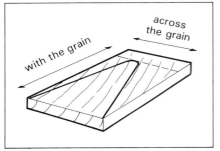

Fig. 4.29

Why should a saw blade need to be flexible?

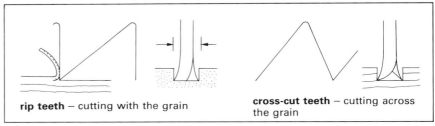

rip teeth – cutting with the grain   **cross-cut teeth** – cutting across the grain

Fig. 4.30

The teeth of a saw are bent outwards or set slightly, in alternate directions, to provide clearance for the blade thickness (see Fig. 4.30). Without this the blade would jam and stick. This happens when the wood is wet and the set is not sufficient to give clearance.

Saws fall into three main groups:

Hand saws – the largest type of saw; very long blades with large teeth. They are used for cutting up large-size material or boards. There are three main types: (a) the rip saw for rough cutting, down the grain; (b) the cross cut for cutting lengths to size; (c) the panel saw for finer cutting of wood or plywood.

Back saws – with a folded metal strip fixed to the top of the blade to keep it straight. They are much smaller than hand saws and have finer teeth. They are ideal for joint cutting and other accurate work. The main types are: tenon saw for general work; dovetail saw for tiny joint work. Both saws have cross-cut teeth.

Frame saws – have very small thin blades, which are stretched or tensioned in a frame of metal or wood. They can cut round curved or awkward shapes. The only limitation is the size of the saw's frame. Fretsaws range from the wood frame bowsaw, used for cutting large size material, to the fine cutting coping saw for more accurate work.

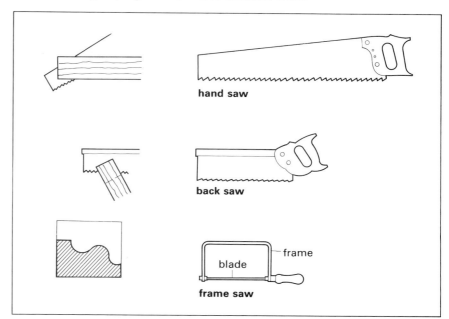

Fig. 4.31

What would happen to the blade in a frame saw if it was not tensioned?

Boring tools

When small holes are to be drilled, up to about 8mm, the metalworkers' twist drill is usually used. These drills cut wood quite well, especially when turned at high speed by the piller or portable electric drill. In the workshop, the slower wheel drill is often used for more accurate and controlled drilling. Large twist drills cut less well, tending to vibrate and chatter and may snatch the wood giving a poor and inaccurate hole.

What would most of the small holes be used for?

Bits

For larger holes, it is the wood workers' bit that is used to remove the wood quickly and easily. To understand how the bit cuts we must break down the cutting action into three parts:

1. The bit has to have a point that will both centre and pull the cutting edges into the wood. This is normally a screw point.

Electric drill

Wheel drill

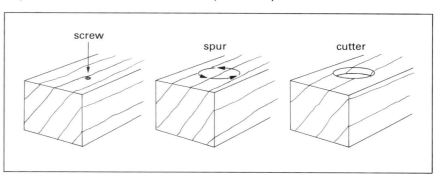

Fig. 4.32   Bit actions

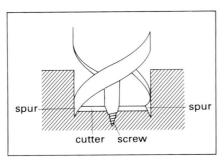

Fig. 4.33

2. It has to have a knife-like edge or *spur* that will cut the wood fibres as the bit revolves. Most modern bits have two spurs.

3. It must have a chisel-like cutting face tht will remove the waste wood. Most modern bits have two cutting faces.

The bit has all these features, and may also have a long helix body to keep it straight when boring deep holes. Several types are manufactured but all use the same cutting action.

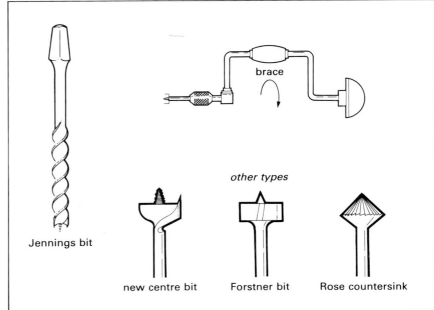

Fig. 4.34

The bit needs a special tool for applying the turning motion and power needed to remove large amounts of wood. This is called a **brace**, and has vee-type jaws for locking onto the square shank of the bit. The brace may have a ratchet system fitted which allows it to be used in confined space when the swing of the brace is restricted.

Wood turning

When a design involves a cylindrical piece of wood, e.g. a round rail or leg for a table or a doorknob, the shaping has to be done on a machine. The wood is spun or turned, while cutting takes place at the same time.

The lathe

A woodworkers' lathe can hold and turn the wood at very high speeds. It is different from the metalworkers' lathe in that the cutting tools are hand held. The speed at which the work turns will depend on (a) how large the work is and (b) how hard the wood is. As a general guide, the smaller the work the faster it should turn, and the harder the wood the slower it should turn.

Why do you think a square shank is used on the brace and not a round system?

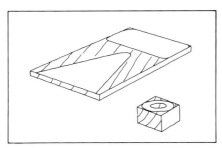

Fig. 4.35

What tools would you use to cut out the shapes in Fig. 4.35?

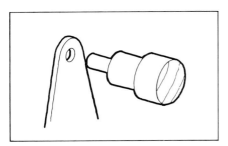

Fig. 4.36

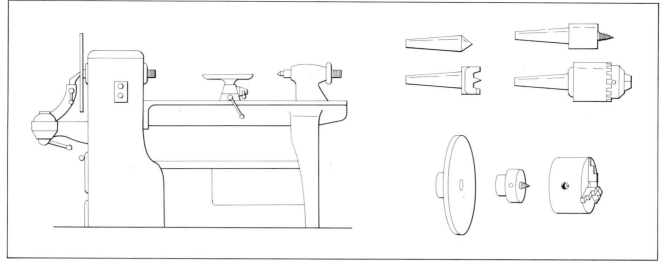

Fig. 4.37 The lathe

Care has to be taken when screwing the face plate to a block of
wood that is to make a dish. Why?

There are two main methods of holding the work on the lathe:

1. screwing it onto a face plate, which in turn is screwed onto the spindle
nose. This is used for small and large flattish objects, such as a bowl, knob,
dish.

2. supporting it between centres, one which drives and the other to hold
steady. This is used for long pieces of work, such as a candlestick, rail or chair
leg.

Once a design has been worked out, a piece of wood has to be prepared.
This has to allow for the lathe holding method which may need extra
material, and also how the grain and shape will match and give the strongest
form.

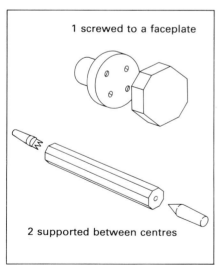

1 screwed to a faceplate

2 supported between centres

Fig. 4.38

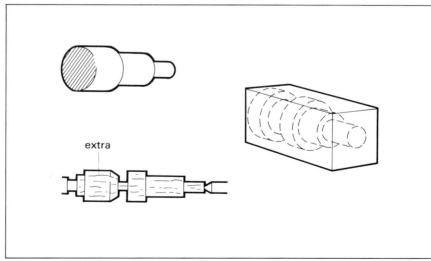

extra

Fig. 4.39

Shaping woods

167

Which block in Fig. 4.40 do you think will, when cut, form the strongest bowl?

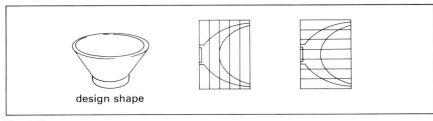

Fig. 4.40

design shape

Great care has to be taken when choosing a suitable wood for turning, as it must be free from knots or splits and must cut easily. Beech, walnut, ash, sycamore and oak are ideal for turning. Some form of eye protection is needed for all wood turning.

The shaping or cutting of the wood is done in two hand-held systems:

Cutting – the surface can be cut by using a very long handled and large size gouge or chisel, held slightly down from the horizontal. As the tool is moved across the work it can quickly rough out the shape required.

An important point to remember is that the tool rest must be as close as possible to the work, to prevent the cutting tool slipping between.

Why should turning tools need long handles?

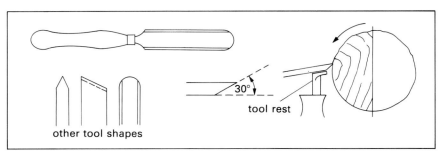

other tool shapes

tool rest

30°

Fig. 4.41

Scraping – similar to the cutting chisels but with a much blunter tip. Old files are sometimes reground into scraping tools (but need careful heat treatment). They are held in a horizontal position and the wood surface is scraped to give a very smooth finish.

Other tool shapes can be ground to a design shape or profile.

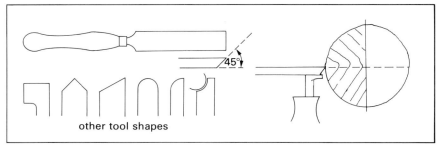

other tool shapes

45°

Fig. 4.42

Faceplate turning

Once the work and faceplate are mounted on the lathe, and the tool rest is set in position and checked, turning can start. The edge is trued by moving the tool from side to side, until a circle is formed.

Shaping now starts to take place, moving the rest at each stage. A card template can be used to check the outside design shape. A small recess is made in the base for locating and fixing the block when it is reversed.

The work is now unscrewed and reversed, using a guide plate to locate and hold. The inside of the shape can now be removed.

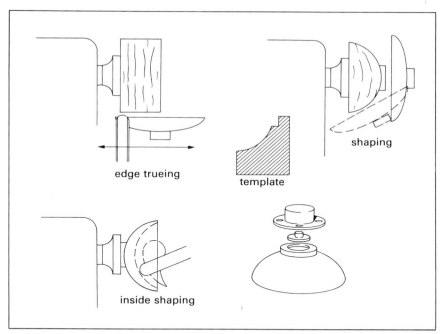

Fig. 4.43

Between centre turning

The work is mounted on the centres, with grease added to the fixed centre to prevent burning. The rest is set in position and checked. Turning starts by roughing down the sides to a cylinder. Once this is done, sizes and details can be marked on the length. The detail shaping now takes place using the scraping tools. Check these with a template for accuracy.

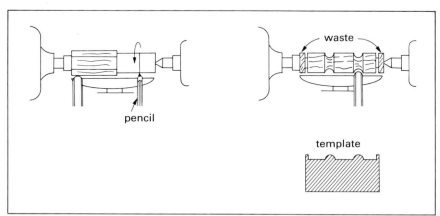

Fig. 4.44   Between centres

Finishing

Before the work is reversed or removed from the lathe it should be given a final finish. This must be done with the tool rest removed, so that it does not get in the way of fingers holding the abrasive paper. The work is rubbed as it

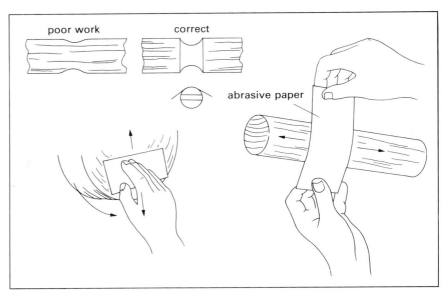

Fig. 4.45 Finishing

Why should burning take place at the fixed centre when turning between centres?

spins, moving the abrasive paper all the time, smoothing down the surface. After working through the different grades of paper, the surface can be sealed and polished or waxed depending on the finish required.

Bending and laminating wood

It is possible to form curves or bends in wood, without having to cut away large amounts of material and leave weak areas of short grain. The method used will depend on how accurate the curve or bend has to be, and how much time and money can be spent. Once a design is worked out, the method of forming the shape must be decided as the wood will have to be prepared and may require special formers to be made.

In what way does bending and laminating wood save material?

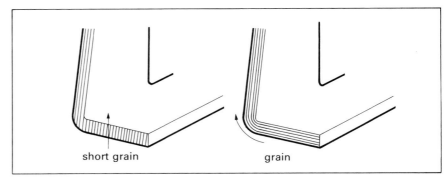

Fig. 4.46

Saw kerfs

This is a simple yet limited way of forming bends. A series of saw cuts are made on the back face of the curve. The saw cuts go to within 3mm of the outer face and are as close together as possible. Once cut, the wood can be bent and then fixed. The curve does tend to show up as a series of tiny flat surfaces, if polished. Stiff plywood or laminated board can be bent in this way.

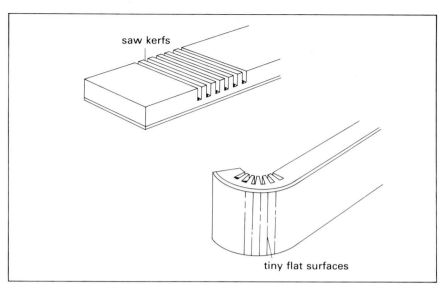

Fig. 4.47

Why does saw kerfing tend to weaken solid wood?

Steam or wet bending

All woods will naturally bend a certain amount without breaking; if they are unseasoned they will bend a great deal more. Bends formed in this way tend to be limited in size and need to be held or the wood returns to a more normal position. If, however, the wood is first heated and softened by hot water or steam, it can be made more pliable and easier to compress. Then if it is held to the shape until dry the wood settles to the curved form.

What do you think are the problems with using boiling water?

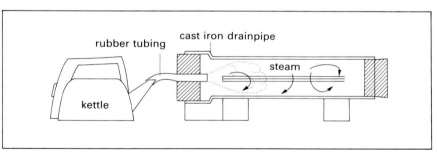

Fig. 4.48

Immersing the wood in boiling water for a period of time is not as successful as using steam. For this, the wood is placed in a special container or steam chest. Steam is passed in to heat the wood to about 100°C. It takes about 45 minutes to soften a piece of 25mm thick material. A simple system can be made up with a kettle, a piece of rubber tubing and a cast iron drainpipe sealed at both ends but with an inlet in one end. It must also have a drainplug, to remove the condensed water before you open the tube.

Once the wood is pliable it has to be used quickly or it will start to stiffen and cool. The bending can be done in a number of ways: the simplest is to mark out the shape on a baseboard and place pegs or blocks at intervals round the outline. The wood is placed in position between the pegs or blocks; or the wood can be trapped, then bent and the pegs added to lock the shape. It is then left to dry. The pegs can leave marks on softwood.

The best method of bending is to use a shaped former and a spring steel band. Quite small bends can be formed without the wood breaking. A solid

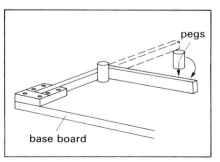

Fig. 4.49

wood former is made up to the inside curved shape. Clamping points also have to be worked out for holding the steamed wood. The steel strap is made to the same width as the steamed wood and clamping handles are screwed to it. It is then pulled round by the handles and again cramped. It is left to dry. The wood will spring back slightly when the cramps are removed – so this has to be allowed for in the former.

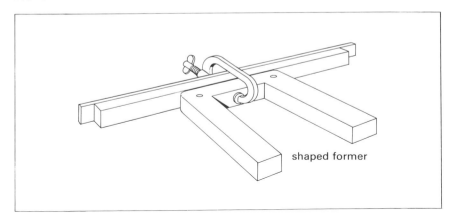

Fig. 4.50

Lamination

The amount that a steamed piece of wood can be bent is limited. The degree of accuracy obtained varies so much that another method has to be used. *Lamination* is much more expensive and more time consuming, but very accurate and has great strength. The shapes are formed by glueing together thin strips of wood – all with the grain running in the same direction – around

Why do you think the *plywood* form of lamination is not suitable for curved shapes?

4 Wood

a former. The strips or laminates bond together to form a permanent accurate shape. It is the building up of these thin strips to the required thickness that makes the method so expensive.

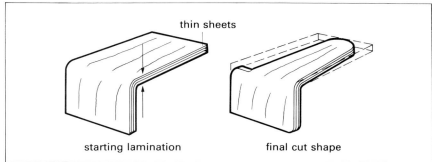

Fig. 4.51

Like steam bending, a number of different ways can be used to form the laminated shape. For a simple shape such as a small salad server, a solid block could be cut up into two formers. These are matching copies of the shape. The strips or laminates are cut to width, slightly longer than needed. Ideal woods are ash, beech, elm and oak — all have natural bending properties. The strips are first cramped up on the formers, dry or without glue, to check that they close together and form the bend. Glue is now spread evenly over the strip faces, and they are placed between the formers with brown paper or polythene on the two outer edges, to prevent the laminate sticking to the mould. The cramps are tightened and any surplus glue is wiped off. It is then left to set.

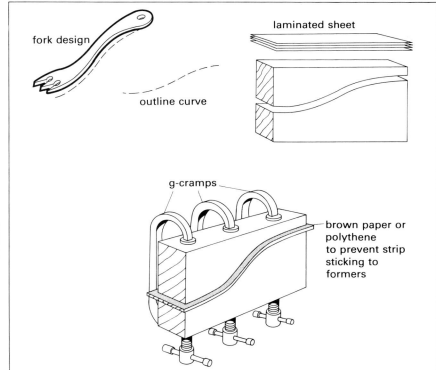

Fig. 4.52

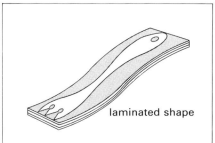

Fig. 4.53

Why do you think the former is
sometimes painted or polished?

On removing the laminated shape from the former any further details can be marked out and cut.

Care has to be taken in using the correct adhesive for the situation in which the final work will be used. This could be, for example, outdoors as part of a sledge or toboggan, or indoors as part of a chair. The following adhesives are suggested:

Total outdoor use — Resorcinol formaldehyde (Aerodux 500 or Cascophen)

Occasional outdoor use — Urea formaldehyde (Aerolite 306 or Cascomite one-shot)

Indoor use — Polyvinyl acetate (Evostik resin 'W') or casein types (Cascomite)

Why do you think that wide
laminates sometimes fail to join in
places using this method?

When wide curved shapes have to be made (e.g. a chair seat) the former has to be built up in place of the solid wood method. Normally manufactured board and softwood strips are screwed together. Once the male former is made, the thin laminates — about 3mm thick — are glued and placed in position. G-cramps are used to hold the laminates down with the aid of blocks: this is to help spread the pressure across the total width. This is left to set, before the cramps are removed.

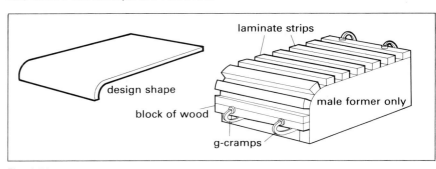

Fig. 4.54

Vacuum bag press

A better method for joining wide laminates is to use a special vacuum bag. This is a rubber bag with an air-extraction system connected. The shaping former is fixed to a baseboard. The laminates are glued and placed together, taping them into the approximate position. The whole assembly is placed inside the bag, and the end is sealed by clamping. Air is drawn from the bag, creating a vacuum; the outside atmospheric pressure forces the bag and laminate down and around the former. The glue is allowed to set before the shape is removed.

Why should the laminates need
taping in position on the former?

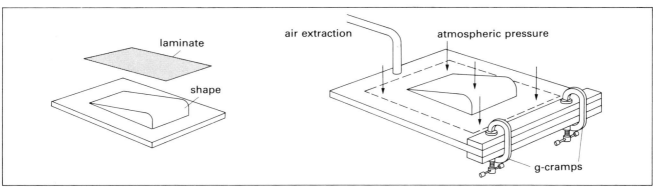

Fig. 4.55   Vacuum bag

Flexible spring steel band

Another very adaptable system is to use a flexible steel band, with metal angle brackets. It works by screwing the brackets to a baseboard on an outline of the shape to be formed. The band is screwed to the brackets, giving a very accurate shape. The laminates are now clamped in a dry run. Once checked and everything correct, the laminates are glued and cramped using g-cramps, rubber pressure pads and wood blocks.

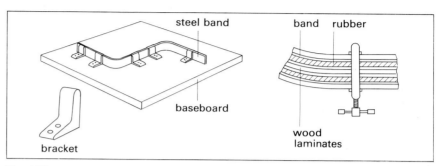

Fig. 4.56

The baseboard is sometimes covered with a polythene sheet. Can you explain why?

The advantage with this system is that the band and angle brackets can be re-used to form other shapes any number of times.

4.7 JOINING WOOD

Why should end grain be so difficult to bond together?

The designer has a vast range of joining methods for wood to choose from: simple glued joints to much more complicated manufactured systems known as 'knock down fittings'. It is for the designer to decide which will be the best method for his or her design.

Adhesives or glues

This must be one of the simplest ways of joining wood. Spread an adhesive over the joining surfaces and hold them together until they bond. The strength of the joint will depend on the type of adhesive and if the two surfaces are a close fit. It is also difficult to bond end grain together. The type of adhesive to use for a design will depend on where and how it is to be used. For example, if the work is to be used out of doors, then the adhesive must be waterproof.

Animal glue (Scotch)

As the name suggests it is derived from the skins and bones of cattle, sheep and horses (brand names: Croid Aero, Sheppy Pearl). It is sold in a thin cake or bead form, and has to be soaked in water, boiled and used hot. It gives a non-staining joint, but has to be applied quickly or it starts to cool and gel. Once applied it will take about 4–6 hours to harden properly so the joint has to be cramped or held together. The main disadvantage is that the glue can be affected by damp or heat, so the joint has a limited use.

Casein glue

The adhesive (brand name: Cascamite) is derived from milk, and is normally obtained in a powder form for mixing with water. It is usually mixed to a thin

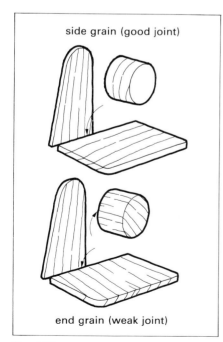

side grain (good joint)

end grain (weak joint)

Fig. 4.57

paste and used cold. It gives a good strong joint which is both heat and waterproof. The main disadvantage is that it will stain many hardwoods (e.g. mahogany, oak and walnut). Setting time is about 4–6 hours and so needs cramping until set.

Synthetic resin glues

This term covers a great many chemical glues which are types of plastics. The two main types used in schools are:

Urea formaldehyde – brand names: Aerolite or Cascamite 'one-shot'. A very strong glue which sets by chemical action. It is water and heatproof and non-staining. It is sold in many forms; the most common being a two-part type which has the resin and hardener separate. The resin is applied to one surface and the hardener to the other. Setting only takes place when the two surfaces are brought together. The bond is formed in about 4–6 hours, so cramping is again needed.

Polyvinyl acetate (PVA) – brand names: Evostik resin 'W', Bostik No. 8. This resin glue is ready mixed for instant use, being in the form of a white cream. It provides a quick setting yet strong non-staining joint, but is not waterproof. The glue sets in about 20–60 minutes, but does not give its full strength until 24 hours later. Once again the joint needs to be cramped.

How can a two-part adhesive give you time to assemble a piece of work before setting?

Contact (impact) adhesives

Brand names include Bostic 1, Dunlop Thixofix, and Evo-Stik 'Impact'. This is not a wood to wood glue, but rather an adhesive for fixing other materials to wood (e.g. plastic laminates, tiles). It is a synthetic rubber-based glue and has to be spread on mating surfaces. It is then left until touch dry. Care has to be taken when joining that the two parts are correctly positioned before bringing them together.

Epoxy resin

Brand names include Araldite and Evo-Stik 'Hard and Fast'. This type of adhesive will bond almost any material; its high cost prevents it being used on large work. It comes in a two-part form: (a) resin, (b) hardener. These have to be mixed together in equal amounts. The mixture is spread over the joining surfaces, and left for 24 hours to set.

Wood joints

Adhesives have limitations when the glueing area is very small or if end grain is involved. To overcome these problems wood joints have been developed over the years. They provide a positive position for pieces, and in some cases act as a locking system, as well as giving a greater glueing surface area.

The type of joint to use in a design will depend on the size of the material and the position at which the pieces will meet.

Carcase or box construction

These are joints in wide material at right angles in a corner. Some of the common methods are as follows:

Butt joint – the two pieces of wood butting together are held by glue and nails (or screws). It is simple but weak, and is only used on poor quality work such as rough boxes.

Rebate joint – a small portion of the wood is removed from one piece, which helps locate the joint. It is glued or nailed or screwed. It is a little stronger than the butt joint.

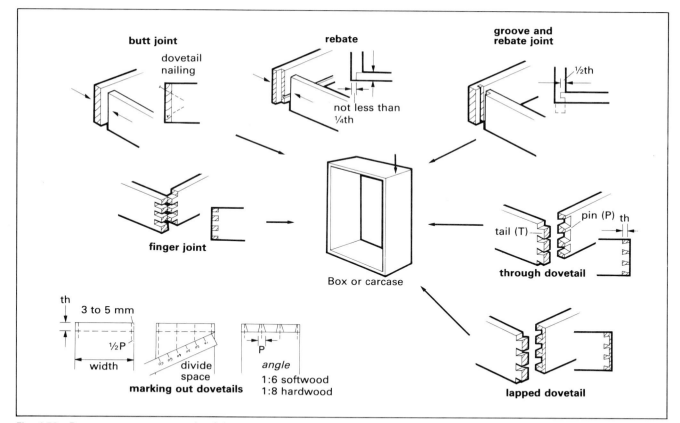

Fig. 4.58 Box or carcase construction joints

Which joint would you use to join the corner on the watch stand (Fig. 4.59)?

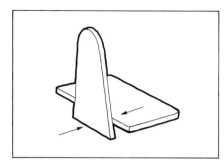

Fig. 4.59

Which joint would be best if a shelf in a cabinet has to help the sides from spreading outwards by holding them?

Rebate and groove joint – a groove is made in one piece and a rebate in the other. This helps to increase the glueing surface and provide a locking system in one direction. Quite a strong joint when glued.

Finger joint – matching fingers provide a large glueing surface, but do not lock.

Dovetail joint – one piece has angled pieces or *tails* cut on the end, which lock between matching pins. This is the strongest method.

Lapped dovetails – hide the end grain on one piece (a secret dovetail hides all the end grain). These joints are used on the very best work as they provide great strength.

Joints in a T-form

The butt joint can be used, but it does not locate the pieces so is only used as a quick but poor method.

Housing joint – a channel is cut out of one piece, in which the second piece can be located. Simple yet strong method when glued or screwed or nailed. The channel can be stopped if a depth position is needed, or the joint line may spoil the look of the work.

Dovetail housing – the channel is cut with angled sides, and the second piece has a dovetail cut. Together they provide a very strong locking system.

Mortise and tenon joint – square or rectangular holes – mortise holes – are cut in one piece and fitting pegs or tenons are cut on the other. Together they form a very strong system and could be used if the work is too thin for a housing type joint. They do not have to be glued but can be held by wedges or dowel. This enables the joint to be taken apart. (See Fig. 4.60 overleaf.)

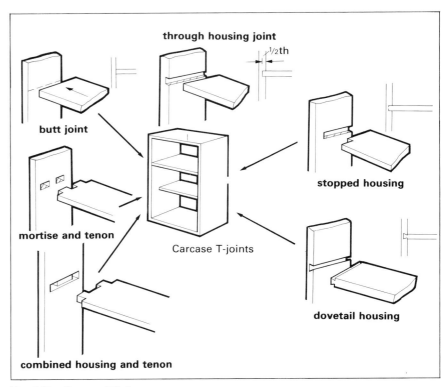

Fig. 4.60   Carcase T-joints

Framework

This is the joining of rectangular section pieces at corners. This method is used for joining such things as picture frames, door frames and window frames. Some of the common methods are as follows:

Halving joint – each joining piece has half its thickness removed, to the width of the material. It provides a good glueing area and location, so the joint is quite good. Removing half the material does, however, tend to weaken the structure. Other forms of halving joints are used e.g. cross-halving, tee-halving, and dovetail halving.

Bridle joint – a rectangular slot is cut out of one piece and a fitting piece is cut on the other. It is stronger than the halving as it provides double the glueing area. The joint can also be used in an intermediate position for a T-joint.

Mortise and tenon joint – strongest of all the frame joints, as it has a large glueing surface but also provides a locating and locking system. A rectangular hole or mortise is cut in one piece and a fitting tenon on the other. The general rule to size is that the tenon is always one third the thickness of the rail. There are different types: through mortise and tenon, stopped mortise and tenon, haunched mortise and tenon – all designed to suit a situation.

Dowelled joint – uses other material to help form the joint: round rod or dowel. The two joining pieces have matching holes drilled in them; the trimmed dowels are glued into position. The system needs accurate positioning of the holes or the pieces do not line up (4.62).

What advantage would a dovetail halving joint have when used?

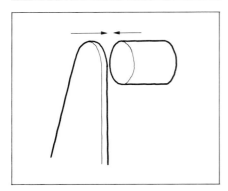

Fig. 4.61

Is it possible to join the above two pieces on the watch stand (Fig. 4.61)?

4   Wood

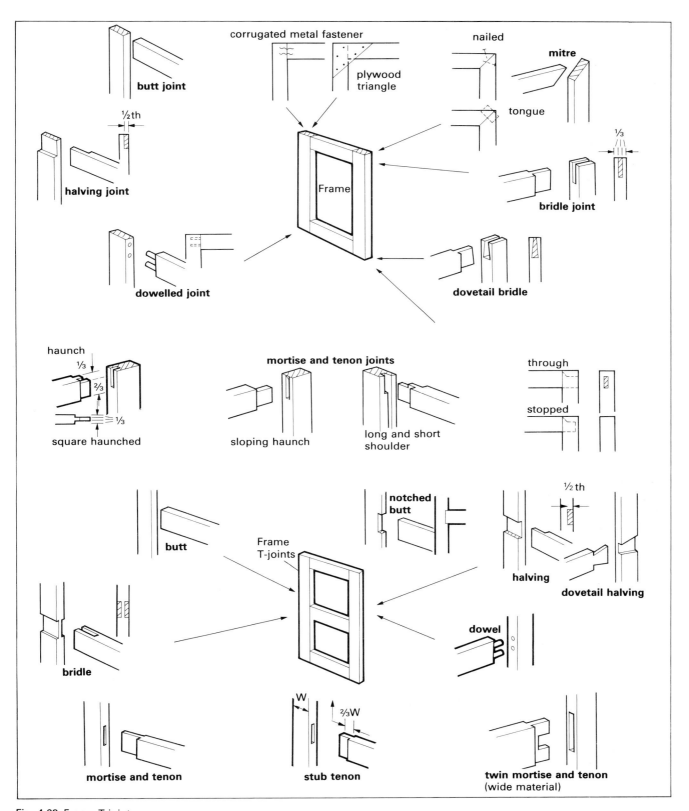

Fig. 4.62 Frame T-joints

Stool and table framework – the main difference with this construction is that two joints occur at the same position. When this happens matching joints have to be mitred to fit e.g. the mortise and tenon (4.63).

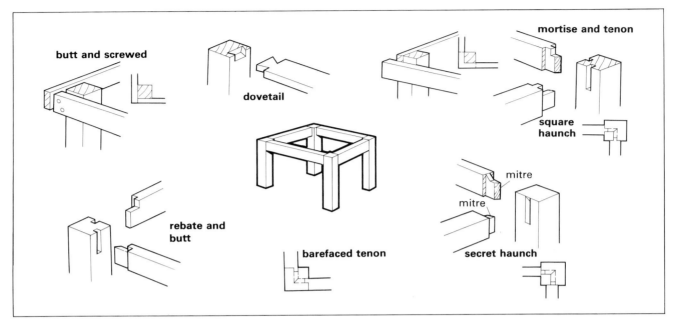

Fig. 4.63 Stool frame construction

Joining wood edge to edge

This is often used to obtain very wide material for such things as table tops, cupboard sides etc. Some of the following methods are used:

Rubbed joint – glueing and butting the two surfaces together after they have been made into a carefully matching fit. The joint depends on how well the two pieces have been fitted.

Loose-tongue joint – the two matching faces have a groove cut in them. A thin strip or tongue is made and they are glued together. The tongue can be of plywood . The joint is very strong and stable; although it is more involved when fitting together.

Tongue and groove joint – only one piece has a groove cut in it; the other is cut to provide the matching tongue. This joint is easy to fit together. It can be glued or left free.

Slot screwed – keyhole slots are cut into one edge; matching screws are fitted to the other. As the boards are fitted, the screw head enters the large hole end. The boards are now driven in opposite directions, to lock.

Dowel joint – as with the corner dowel system, matching holes and dowels form the joint.

What problems can you see if some of these joints are used on manufactured boards?

4 Wood

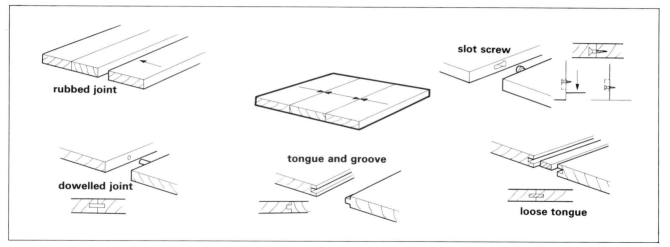

Fig. 4.64   Joining wood

These are some of the joints used for joining wood to wood. In many cases they will combine together on a piece of work to hold several items.

Fixing boards or tops to frames

It is possible to fix a board or top to an underframe by simply nailing or screwing from the top. However this does spoil the appearance of the frame surface. Other methods are used to hide the fixing system, and in some cases to allow for wood movement, such as shrinkage or expansion, which could buckle the surface.

Pocket screwing – angled holes are drilled through the underframe rails and countersunk. Screws can now be fixed from the underside into the board or top. This method does not allow for any wood movement.

Fixing plates – brass or steel plates are recessed into the underframe rails and screwed into position. The slotted end of the plate can then be fixed to the underside of the board or top. The slot allows for any wood movement that may occur.

Turn button – little wood buttons are made and fixed into the underside of the board or top. Small matching slots are cut into the underframe rails. The buttons are then turned into the slot to fix. This system allows for wood movement.

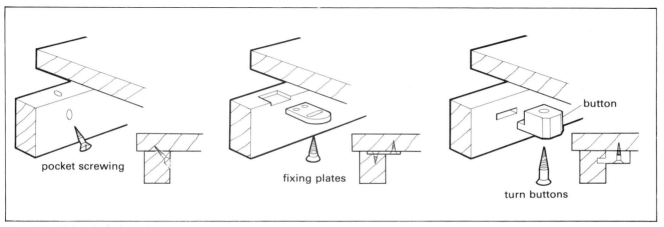

Fig. 4.65   Fixing boards to frames

Joining wood

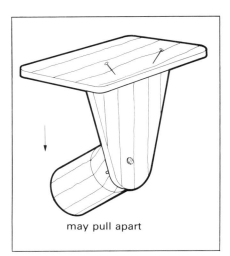

Fig. 4.66 Watch stand

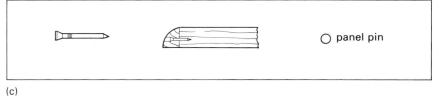

Why should a nail hold better in side grain than in end grain?

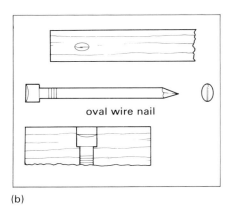

(b)

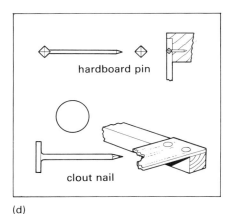

(d)

Nails

These are metal pins with heads that can be used for joining wood very quickly. They are, however, unsightly unless punched below the surface and hidden. They have small serrations or burrs on the shank, which when driven into the wood catch on the fibres. The joint has good strength but can pull open if pressure or force is applied. In the main, nails are made from mild steel and can be obtained in many different forms and sizes, each designed for a particular function. They are sold by weight, so the number you obtain will depend on type, length and material. Some of the most common are:

Round wire nail

This is a general purpose nail with a large round head. It is used mainly for joining rough work which needs a strong nail with good holding power. The disadvantage is that the head is unsightly and is difficult to sink into the surface. Sizes: 20–150mm.

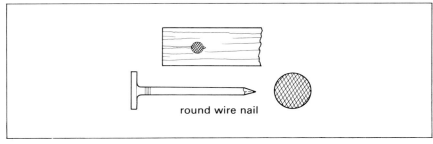

Fig. 4.67(a)

Oval wire nail

A much finer nail, oval in shape with a small head, which allows the head of the nail to be punched below the surface. It is less likely to split the wood than a round nail so can be used on finer work. Sizes: 12–150mm.

Panel pin

This is a very fine nail with a tiny head. It is used for light delicate work such as edging or beading. It can also be driven below the surface and hidden. Sizes: 12–50mm.

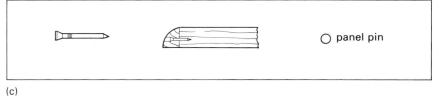

(c)

Hardboard pin

A square shank nail with a diamond-shaped head that can be driven into hardboard without bending. Sizes: 9–40mm.

Clout nail

A very large headed nail suitable for fixing soft material such as roofing felt. They are normally galvanised for outdoor use. Size: 12–50mm.

Tack

A very short but large-headed nail that is either blued or tinned to prevent rusting. It is used for holding most upholstery materials. Sizes: 6–30mm.

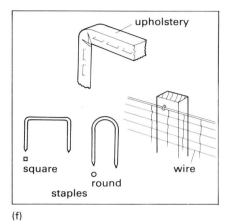

(f)

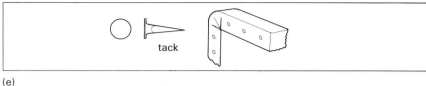

tack

(e)

Staples

A quick method of holding work; square for upholstery, round for wire or springs. The square type are fired into the wood by a special staple gun; the round type are fixed with a hammer. Various sizes.

These are only a few of the nails available. When using nails certain points should be noted if you want to gain the joint required. See Fig. 3.73 for some useful hints.

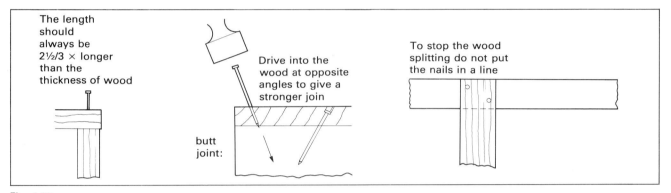

The length should always be 2½/3 × longer than the thickness of wood

Drive into the wood at opposite angles to give a stronger join

butt joint:

To stop the wood splitting do not put the nails in a line

Fig. 4.68

Screws

The designer sometimes needs a method of joining that is not permanent and yet has maximum holding power. Screws fit this role perfectly, as they have much better holding power than nails and can be removed easily. They have a tapered body which has a sharp twist or helix thread; this screws itself into the wood fibres and can only be removed by unscrewing.

Many types of screw are available – made from mild steel or brass and may be coated for protection or decoration (e.g. black japanned, galvanised, chromium plated). The head shapes vary, as does the method of turning the

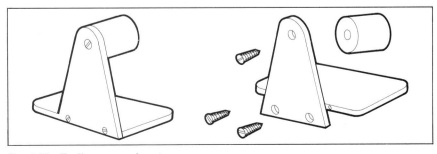

Fig. 4.69   Easily removed system

Brass screws are not as strong as mild steel screws. Why are they used?

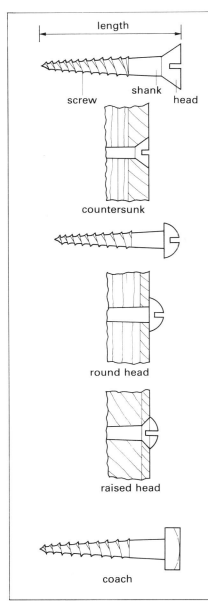

Fig. 4.70 Screws

Why do you think paint or dirt in a pozidriv head would affect the working?

screw. The screw size is determined by its shank diameter (or gauge). Its length is from the head rim to thread tip. Gauge numbers (4, 6, 8,10 etc.) stay the same, whatever the length. Screws are sold in boxes of 100, 200 etc. The common screws are:

Countersunk head screw

A general purpose screw that is used when a flush surface finish is required. The work to be joined does require a countersunk hole for the screw to sit flush, which can weaken thin material. Sizes: 6.5–150mm.

Round head screw

This is mainy used for fixing other fittings to wood, such as metal strip or plastic. It has the advantage of not weakening the material by countersinking, but will not give the flush finish. Quite often they are black japanned for protection when they are to be used out of doors. Sizes: 6.5–87mm.

Raised head screw

A decorative screw that holds like a countersunk, but gives the round head finish. It is used for holding such things as door handles, cupboard catches, letter plates. For this reason they are coated to match the fitting e.g. chromium or nickel. Sizes: 8–50mm.

Twinfast screw

This is a screw that was developed for manufactured boards such as chipboard and blockboard. It has two threads so that it is easier to insert and provides stronger holding power. Sizes: 6.5–87mm.

Coach screw

This is the largest of all the screws and has to be turned with a spanner. It is used for heavy constructions and frames. Sizes: 25–406mm.

Turning screws

These are manufactured in three forms:

Slotted head – the most common and simplest method. It has a straight slot cut across the top of the screw. The screwdriver can, however, slip and damage the surrounding wood or screw. It can be removed with any flat object (e.g. a coin), so valuable items or fittings can be removed without much trouble.

Phillips head – needs a special screwdriver to fit and turn. It has a crossed recessed slot. It is a better system than the straight slot because it is more secure, and the screwdriver has less chance of slipping.

Pozidriv head – an improved version of the Phillips head. It also has a crossed recess but with an added grip system.

Fig. 4.71 Turning screws

Fitting screws

Before screws can be fitted, the work has to be drilled. A hole is first made the same size as the screw shank. This is called a *clearance hole*. It may be countersunk if needed. The work is now positioned together and a *pilot hole*, about half the size of the clearance hole, is drilled into the holding place. The length of the screw should be 2½ to 3 times longer than the thickness of the object to be held.

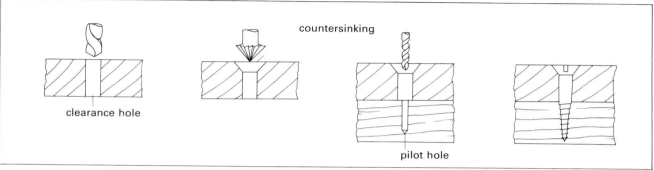

Fig. 4.72 Fitting screws

When screwing into end grain or manufactured board the screw fails to grip well. To overcome this two simple methods can be used.

Plastic wall plug – in place of the pilot hole a hole is drilled for a plastic wall plug which matches the screw to be used. The plug is inserted and the screw is fitted. The plug expands and grips the side of the hole.

Dowel – if the wood or board is not too wide, a hole can be drilled at right angles to the direction of the screws. Into this can be glued a wooden dowel. This provides side grain for the screw to grip into.

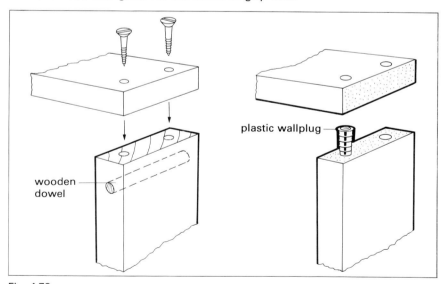

Fig. 4.73

What type of furniture do you think the KD fittings would be used on?

Knock down fittings

The use of manufactured boards (chipboard, blockboard) in modern furniture and the growing interest in self-assembly, has led to a whole new range of joining methods. These have become known as KD or 'knock down fittings'.

They allow the work to be assembled or pulled apart as many times as required, without weakening the joint or the material. Some of the most common types are as follows:

Corner blocks

A matching set of nylon blocks are screwed to the inside of the joining sides. A central screw locks them together. They work quite well but look unsightly.

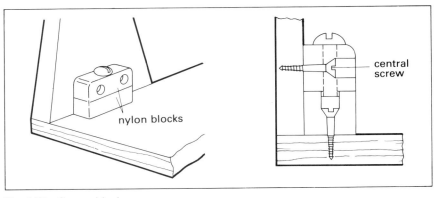

Fig. 4.74 Corner blocks

Barrel and screw

A nylon or metal barrel is fitted into a drilled hole in one piece, the other is drilled to take a machine screw. The screw is tightened into the barrel. Do not use in weak end grain or chipboard. A dowel should be used alongside the screw to prevent twisting.

Self-locking plates

Each plate is screwed to the joining sides. Then, as they are pushed together, a springing action locks them together.

Corner plate and screw bolt

A central screw bolt is fitted into the corner piece or leg. The side pieces or rails are slotted for the plate and have normal joints cut on the end. The joint is fitted together dry, the plate located over the bolt end and a wing nut tightens the whole unit together.

Joining different materials

Designers often find that a joint has to be made between wood and other materials. The most common type of joint needed is between wood and metal tubing. Items such as screws and KD fittings can be used again. Some simple methods are as follows:

Slot method – a slot in the metal tube; wood cut with side slots. The two are driven together to form a tight joint.

Lug method – tube has a thin strip or lug welded onto the side face; wooden rail is cut with a matching notch. The joint can be bonded with an epoxy resin or dowels used through drilled holes.

Dowel method – end tube is fitted with a wooden block – fixed in place with epoxy resin. The tube and wooden rail are drilled as for a normal dowel joint and the dowels fitted to complete the joint.

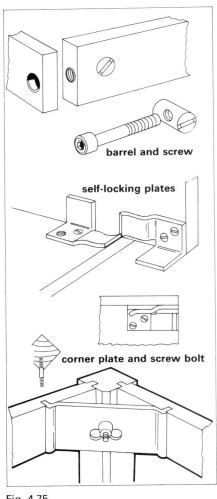

barrel and screw

self-locking plates

corner plate and screw bolt

Fig. 4.75

Why does epoxy resin have to be used for the dowel joint?

4 Wood

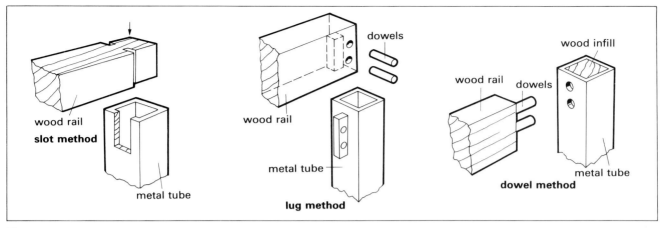

Fig. 4.76

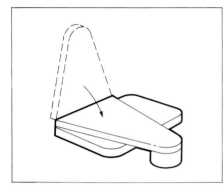

Fig. 4.77

What sort of hinge should we use on our watch stand

Other wood fittings

When a moving joint is needed between two parts, **hinges** have to be used. These can be made from steel, brass or nylon. They can have galvanised or japanned finishes. The range of hinges available is vast, but some of the most common are:

Butt hinge – most common type; used for doors, cabinets, windows, screens. It is usually recessed into the two joining parts (door and frame), to give a neat, close finish.

Flush hinge – lightweight and does not need to be recessed. It is used for light doors or screens.

Back flap hinge – a stronger hinge than the butt, having larger flaps and spaced screw holes. It is used for drop-down work such as bureau flaps, table leaves and box lids.

Continuous hinge (piano) – lightweight; designed to be cut to the length of the joining pieces, thus spreading the weight. It is also used for cabinet lids or chests.

T-hinge – can carry quite heavy loads, by spreading the weight over a long arm. It is used for such things as tool cupboards, gates, and garage doors.

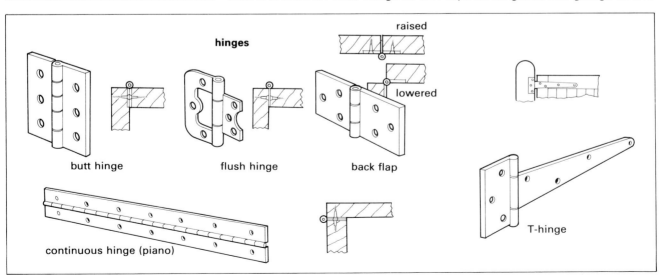

Fig. 4.78a) Other wood fittings

The hinge provides the moving joint, but we also need a **catch** to hold the work when not in use. Here are a few:

Turn button – simple button fitted to the fixed part (frame). It can be turned to prevent the moving part (door) from going past.

Ball catch – much neater method than the turn button. It is fitted into the edge of the moving part (door) with a catch plate recessed into the fixed part. As the two parts close the sprung ball moves and then catches.

Magnetic catch – works with a strong magnet fitted to one part and a plate fitted to the other. Its main advantage is that it is silent.

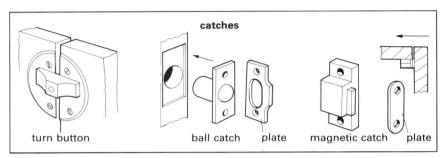

Fig. 4.78(b)

To secure work in a more permanent way, **locks** can be fitted. A wide range are available. Here are a few:

Cupboard lock – simple steel or brass lock, fitted to the inside of a cupboard door.

Drawer lock – recessed into the edge of the work, making a neater finish.

Box lock – used when the two parts could be pulled apart, such as a box lid. The hooks on the keeper engage on the bolt when the key is turned.

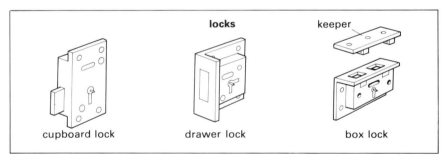

Fig. 4.78(c)

4.8 FINISHING WOOD

Wiping surplus glue from work helps the process of finishing. How?

When any wood is used in a piece of design work, the way it is to be finished and left for use has to be thought out very carefully. This is important as it will play an important part in:
1. keeping the wood clean;
2. keeping out moisture, and so preserving the wood;
3. adding to the appearance.

Why should a knot present a problem when smoothing the surface?

But before any finish can be applied, the wood has to be prepared. This involves making the wood surfaces as clean and as smooth as possible, free from marks, scratches, glue etc.

It is possible to obtain a very good surface using a well-sharpened smoothing plane which has been set to take very fine shavings. Softwoods, in particular, can be prepared in this way, if free from too many knots.

Scraper

When woods have difficult grains to smooth or when the smoothing plane is leaving marks on the surface, the work has to be finished with a scraper. The scraper in fact cuts, taking a very fine shaving of wood but leaving a very good smooth finish. It has tiny burred or sharp edges on a flat steel plate. It is passed over the surface, held by either hand or holder. Hardwoods and thin veneers are best prepared in this way.

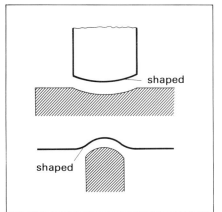

Fig. 4.80 Special scrapers

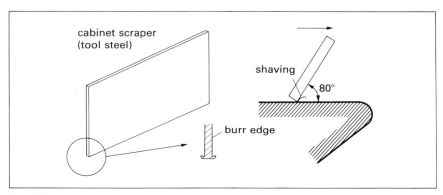

Fig. 4.79

If a smoothing plane was used to prepare a veneered surface, what would be the problem?

The normal scraper is rectangular with flat sides; however, special shapes that have to be prepared can have scrapers ground in the workshop using the grindstone.

Abrasive paper

This is perhaps the best known method of preparing wood, using either glasspaper (particles of glass on a paper backing) or garnet paper (crushed garnet stone on a paper backing). When these are rubbed over the wood surface they give a smooth finish. They can spoil work if used badly, causing scratches and removing parts of a fine shape. This is why the papers are made in different grades: coarse for rough rubbing down of a surface when starting; down to a very fine grade for careful finishing.

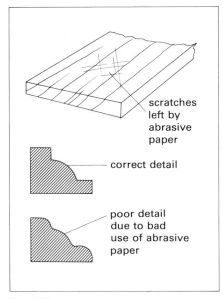

Fig. 4.81

Grade of abrasive paper	Glass paper	Garnet paper
coarse	3	2
	2½	1½
	S2	1
	M2	½
medium	F2	0
	1½	2/0
fine	1	3/0
	0	4/0
	00	5/0
extra fine	FLOUR	6/0

Why is it best to use a block and not just your hand?

To use the paper correctly it should be wrapped round a cork or wood block. This can be rectangular or shaped to the work being prepared. The block should be rubbed in the direction of the grain to prevent scratching.

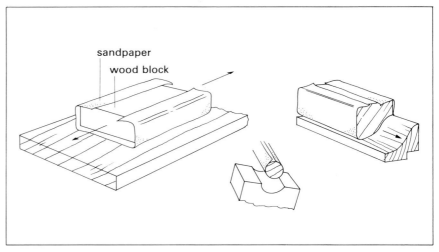

Fig. 4.82

Some grain may lift when polish is applied due to it being pushed flat and not cut by the abrasive paper. This can be overcome by damping the wood surface, and sandpapering again when dry. If this is repeated a number of times, a very smooth surface can be obtained.

Wire wool (steel wool) is used in the final stages of finishing or polishing, as a very fine abrasive (e.g. when rubbing down a lacquer finish before waxing).

Staining or colouring

It is possible to colour or stain wood in an attempt to make it look brighter or to match some existing work. It should only be done as a last resort, as most woods are more attractive if left with their natural colour. The stain or colour when applied is not a final finish, and the wood will need some sealing or protective coating. For this reason, care has to be taken in choosing the correct type of stain for the finish that will follow, as a chemical reaction can sometimes take place between the two.

Care should be taken not to spill drops of stain on a wood surface. Why?

Water-based stains are the best when in doubt; although oil-based stains last longer. It is always best to try out the stain on a scrap sample of the wood, so that a check can be made. Several coats can darken a piece of wood a little more.

Grain filling

Some wood finishes require a very flat surface before they can be applied, if they are to give the best appearance possible; for example, french polish, lacquer and paint. Other finishes are better if the wood is left natural (e.g. oil and wax). Two main types of fillers are used:

Whitening or china clay – mixed with turpentine or methylated spirit to a thin paste. This is used for polished or lacquered surfaces.

Lead-based fillers – used for painted surfaces; however, leadless fillers have to be used when the surface may come into contact with small children (e.g. cots). These fillers are also in a paste form and can be applied with a rag or flat knife tool. They are left to dry and harden before being smoothed down with an abrasive paper.

Why could lead-based fillers be dangerous to children?

Oil finish

When a natural appearance is required, one method is to apply an oil to the wood surface. This highlights the wood's own colour and grain, making it water-resistant with a non-shine finish. Several different oils can be used:

Olive oil

This would be used as a finish when the wood is going to come into contact with food (e.g. a bread board or salad servers), due to the fact that it is both odourless and harmless.

Linseed oil

This is a much less expensive oil that can be used on most woods, other than beech, ash, and pines which become dirty and discoloured very quickly. It is normally mixed with turpentine to speed up the drying and needs to be applied in 2–4 coats for the best protection.

Teak oil

As the name suggests this oil is ideal for such woods as teak, afromosia and iroka. It contains quick drying agents and varnishes that speed up the drying time and greatly improve the standard of protection.

Most oil finishes are applied with a cloth, worked across the grain. After about an hour the surface is wiped clean with a second cloth and left to dry. Forty-eight hours later, a second application is given and again cleaned and left to dry. Hard rubbing with a soft cloth can build up a sheen over a period of time.

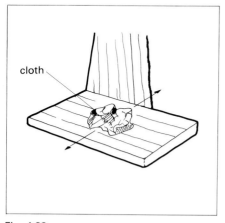

cloth

Fig. 4.83

Why should the wax polish be left some time before rubbing up?

Wax polish

This is another natural-looking finish that uses beeswax/carnauba wax mixed with turpentine or silicone and driers. The wax is applied in a paste form, using a cloth. Before the wax is applied, the surface has to be sealed with a cellulose sealer; if not, the finish will not last. Once the sealer is dry it is rubbed down lightly with a fine grade sandpaper, brushed, and given a coat of wax. This is worked into the piece with a soft cloth and then left for several hours before polishing up is started, again with a cloth or soft brush. The more the finish is applied, the better the surface becomes.

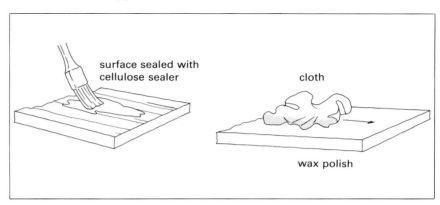

surface sealed with cellulose sealer

cloth

wax polish

Fig. 4.84

Polyurethane lacquer

This is a synthetic resin or liquid plastic that dries to give a clear but very tough surface finish. It has the advantage over the clear type finishes in that it is heat, water and spirit proof, and will stand up to hard knocks. It can be bought in two forms:

Two-pack – comes with the lacquer and catalyst separate. They can be mixed as required so that less is wasted. When mixed as the manufacturer has stated, it is allowed to stand for a few minutes before using.

One-pack – comes ready-mixed and must be used once it is exposed to air. This can be wasteful if more than is needed has been opened from a container.

The lacquer can be applied with a brush or spray. It is better to apply thin coats rather than one thick layer. It should be left for about 12 hours to cure or set, before it is lightly sanded and a second coat applied. The final coat can also be gently rubbed down with a fine grade steel wool and a thin coat of wax polish given.

French polish

This is one of the oldest forms of finishing wood, giving a beautiful surface finish. However, it does require great skill and time to apply the polish, as the finish is only built up after a large number of layers have been applied and worked. The final finish will not stand up to heat such as a hot plate. Many liquids will also stain or mark the final surface, so the surface must be looked after.

The polish is made up of shellac dissolved in methylated spirit, and comes in different tones of brown. These are known as button, garnet, white and transparent.

Before polishing, the wood surface is grain filled and smoothed. Using a special rubber or cotton wool wrapped inside a linen cover charged with polish, the surface is given a thin coat. This is allowed to dry for a few minutes, before a second application is given. This is repeated over and over again until a good level surface is obtained. To complete the finish, the surface is left for about 8 hours, before being **spirited off**. This is cleaning the surface with a fresh rubber that has been damped with methylated spirit. In doing so it removes all the rubbing marks, leaving a high gloss surface finish.

Paint

When a piece of design work requires a bright-coloured finish and a degree of protection, paint is used. It tends to be the softwoods that are painted as the hardwoods cover less well and look more interesting when left naturally. The colour range is large, and is covered by a British Standard, so that all makers conform to one colour code or chart. Several different types are available from flat non-shine to very high gloss.

Emulsion paints

These contain a vinyl or acrylic resin that can be water thinned. They cover wood very well, but are not very durable or weatherproof. The colour tends to be pale and dull (matt finish); some have a slight shine (silk finish).

Oil paints

This type of paint is mainly made up of boiled linseed oil with coloured pigments added. Sometimes silicone is added to help surface cleaning, and polyurethane to increase surface hardness. White spirit is used as a thinner,

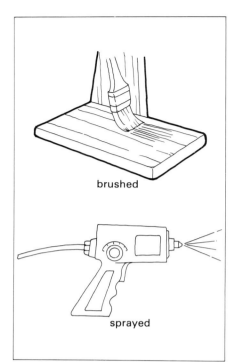

brushed

sprayed

Fig. 4.85 Polyurethane lacquer

Polyurethane lacquer can be dangerous if used as a floor polish. Why should this be?

What are the different ways that paint can be applied?

What would you consider to be the best finish for a mahogany watch stand?

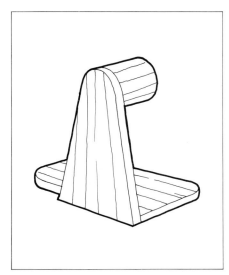

Fig. 4.86

Some oil paints contain lead. How could this be dangerous when used for woodwork?

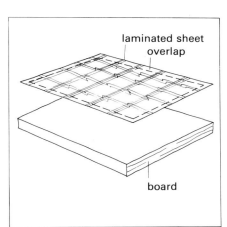

Fig. 4.88

It is normal to glue the sheet in place. What problems would nailing and screwing cause?

although some paints are sold in a gel or non-drip form.

The wood is sealed with a priming coat, then an undercoat, before the final colour coat is applied. This can take the form of a high gloss, semi-gloss or a matt finish: all are suitable for indoors or outdoors, being waterproof and durable. The colours are bright and stay this way for years.

Polyurethane paint

The most common type is the one-pack form (resin with catalyst). Once it is exposed to air the chemical reaction starts and hardening takes place. The paint is very tough and scratch-resistant, and can stand quite high temperatures without being damaged. It is an ideal paint for such things as toys, furniture, doors and any place that has to take rough treatment.

Before painting starts the wood is glasspapered. Then a solution of shellac and methylated spirit is coated over any knots. This is to seal them and stops any resin from oozing out. The surface is now primed with a base of paint and allowed to dry. All holes or tiny marks are filled with a water-resistant filler and left to harden. The surface is now glasspapered smooth and wiped clean with a damp rag.

The undercoat of colour is then applied as an even layer and again allowed to dry, before glasspapering the surface again. Once it has been cleaned, the final coat (gloss, matt or semi-gloss) is applied; two if a high standard of protection is required.

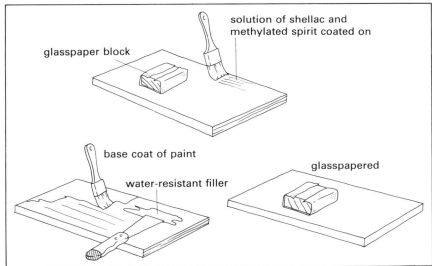

Fig. 4.87

Laminated plastics

When a wood surface is to be used constantly and may be subjected to hard wear, the polished type finishes or paints are unable to cope. This problem is overcome by adding a laminated plastic sheet to the surface (e.g. Formica or Warerite). Layers of resin-impregnated paper are bonded together under high pressure to form a sheet. It is very hard and smooth, which makes it an excellent wipe clean surface. As the sheet is used in prominent positions such as kitchen work tops, it normally has a bright colour design on the upper surface.

The sheet can be damaged by very hot items such as cooking pans, and sharp tools such as knives.

To lay the sheet it must first have a prepared base board that is both flat and true, e.g. chipboard, blockboard or plywood. The laminated sheet is cut to size, with a slight overlap at the edges. A rubber-based contact adhesive (e.g. Evostik) is spread thinly over the base and underside of the laminated sheet. It is left until it is touch dry. The two surfaces are then carefully positioned together with equal overlap at the edges and pressed down. The edges of the top surface may also need to match or be protected. These can also be covered with a thin strip of laminated plastic and glued into position. Once both top and edges are bonded the overlapping edges can be trimmed with a file.

Chapter 5

SAFETY

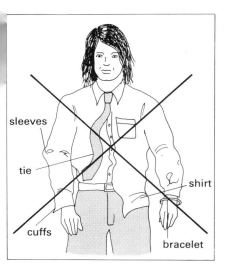

sleeves

tie

shirt

cuffs

bracelet

Fig. 5.1

Long hair can also be a problem in the workshop when it comes to safety. What dangers do you think this could cause? What steps could you take to prevent an accident?

Once all the design work has been completed for a project, the practical aspect can start. This will involve using different workshops, materials, tools and processes. If the work is to progress safely certain areas of risk should be noted at the start. This not only applies to the person making the object but also to others who may be close by.

Personal clothing and appearance

As much of the practical work will involve getting messy and dirty, some form of protection is needed for normal clothes. An apron or overall will give this protection, as well as keeping loose items of clothing such as a tie from getting caught in a revolving part or machine. Sleeves and cuffs should be rolled up and items such as a watch or a bracelet should be removed.

Before starting any practical work it is wise to check if any special clothing or protection is needed.

Hand protection

Hands should always be covered with a barrier cream to help with the washing or cleaning when the work is completed. It will also prevent skin diseases protecting against wood dust, plastic resins, etc.

Gloves or tongs for holding hot metal

Eye protection

Any process which involves small particles being thrown from the work can cause damage to eyes. This can range from fine dust or grit (from cutting, sanding, grinding) to large waste particles (from machining). It could also come from using dangerous chemicals or liquids, such as mixing in a catalyst for Glass Reinforced Plastics (GRP) work or dipping metal into an acid bath for cleaning.

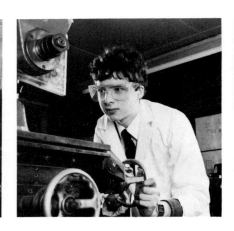

What other workshop processes can you think of which cause fumes?

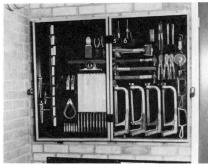

Nose and mouth protection

Dust can be inhaled if it is in a fine form. This can be very harmful, causing breathing problems. Some of the processes also give off fumes, which can be unpleasant and, in some cases, poisonous. For example, when expanded polystyrene is cut with a hot wire cutter it gives off fumes that can cause dizziness and sickness.

Before starting any workshop processes that involve using heat, liquids, chemicals and machine work, make sure the room is well ventilated. This means opening a window or doors, to give a good circulation of air.

People working close to the process must wear a disposable breathing mask or respirator, so that the air and fumes or dust are filtered.

These are the main forms of personal protection. Others are used – e.g. leggings, ear muffs, special shoes – but not so often.

The workshop

The key to safety in the workshop is to keep it clean and tidy. Do not misuse the tools. Act in a responsible manner. Loose materials such as wood, metal or plastic left on the floor or propped against a bench may cause accidents. The floor should be clear. Mop up any grease, oil, adhesive or resin which has been spilt. All materials should be stored in a separate room with special care being taken with those which have a high fire risk e.g. plastic resins, foams, petrol.

Tools should be used, then returned to their racks or cupboard. They should not be allowed to pile up on a bench or machine. Sharp tools hidden under shavings or waste material, can be dangerous.

Work should always be held securely by some form of clamp or vice before cutting, drilling and all machine processes. Any adjustments to the work or cutting tools should only be done when the machine has been stopped.

The final clearing up of the bench, machine or workshop must be done with the correct tools. Never use your bare hands!

In general, the workshop is a safe place. If commonsense is used, accidents will not happen. If all slight cuts, scratches and splinters are treated immediately, infection cannot start.

Part Three

Design problem examples

6.1   MARBLE GAME

An observed problem is that doctors' and dentists' waiting rooms are usually rather dull and boring places and something is needed to take people's minds off their problems. It is thought that perhaps some form of simple game would help to amuse and interest children and adults while they are waiting. As space is limited it would have to be confined to a simple box, about 250 x 175 x 50mm in size, so that it could be stored easily when not in use.

Design brief

Design a simple box game about 250 x 175 x 50mm that will keep children and adults amused while they are waiting in a doctor's or dentist's waiting room.

This is how one boy solved the problem.

The waiting room	Answer	Possible research needed
Analysis		
(a) What are waiting rooms like?	Normally small and quiet	Visit both types of waiting room
(b) What type of furniture is used in a waiting room?	Upright wooden chairs and a low table	Check chairs and tables, material and sizes
(c) What are the possible positions for the game in the room	(1) fixed to the wall (2) resting on the table	Check what wall space is free
Children and adults		
(a) How will they affect the game?	(1) the position of the game (2) the handling of the game (3) the complexity	Check the height range Check weight and size
(b) What is the best position for the game, bearing in mind the vast age range?	As the wall height may be a problem, resting on the table seems best	Check if it is possible to fix to a table
The game		
(a) What is a game?	A contest bound by rules and decided by skill, strength or luck	Define the word 'game'
(b) What possible indoor games could fit into a box?	(a) a ball game (b) a board game (c) a card game	Check range of games
(c) How difficult should the game be?	It will need to be quite simple with few rules, yet prove to be interesting	What games would fit this? Check with your range of games
(d) What game would you use?	From the research a marble game would seem best	Different forms of marble game
The box		
(a) What material could the box be made from?	Wood, metal or plastic, but depends on how box is to be used. If handled, needs to be light, robust, with safe edges	List possible materials under each heading
(b) What safety points need to be considered?	Box material needs to be hygienic and easy to clean, with a non-toxic finish	
(c) What type of construction should be used?	Depends on the material being used, but it must be simple yet strong	Check box construction in the three materials
(d) What type of surface finish should be used?	As the box is indoors, it does not need to be waterproof, but it will need to be hard wearing	Check surface finishes

Table 17

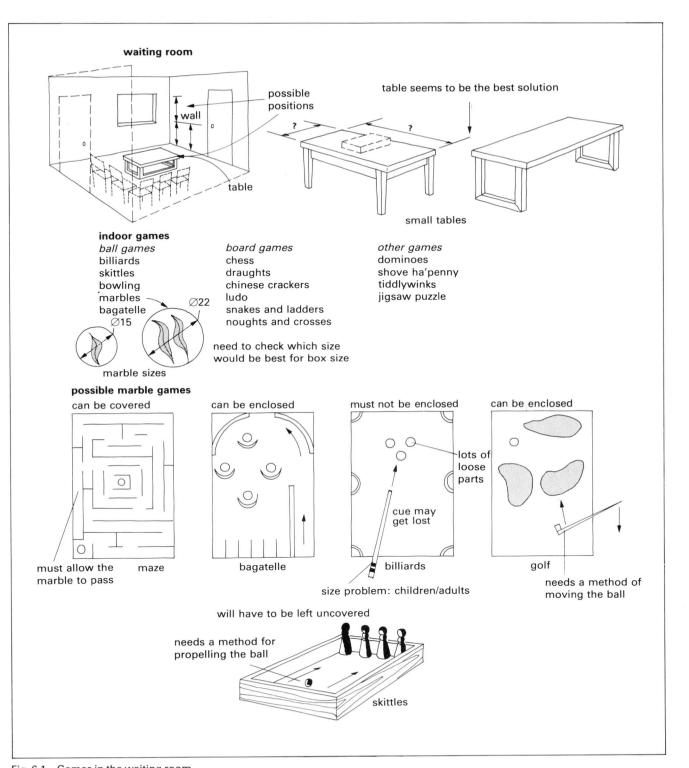

Fig. 6.1   Games in the waiting room

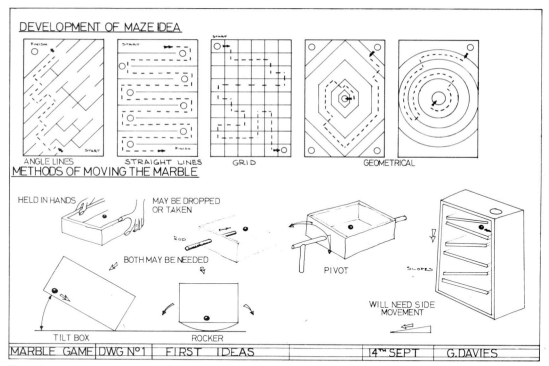

Fig. 6.2

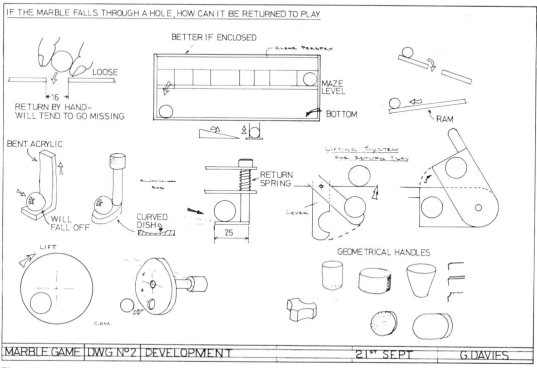

Fig. 6.3

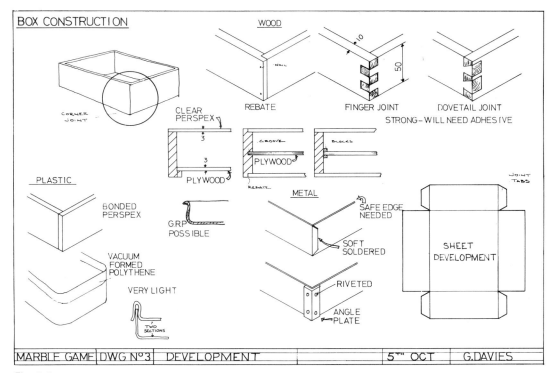

Fig. 6.4

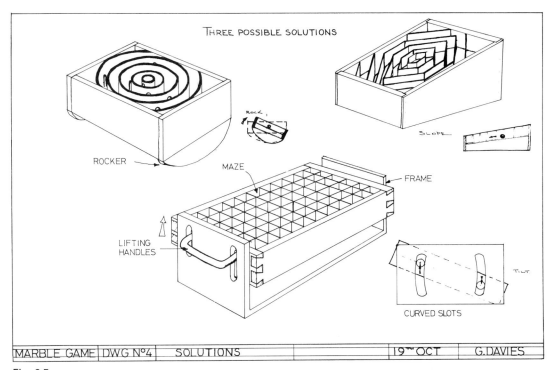

Fig. 6.5

Marble game

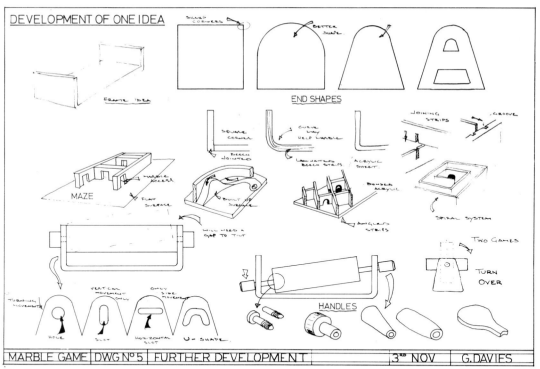

Fig. 6.6

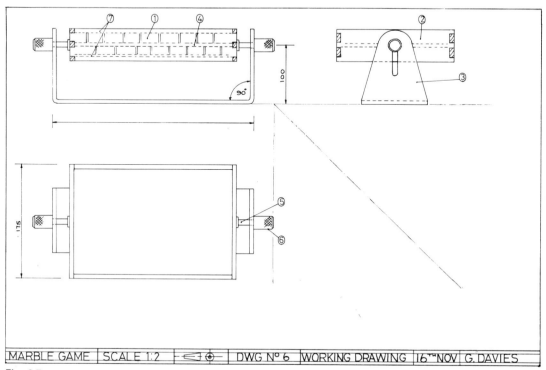

Fig. 6.7

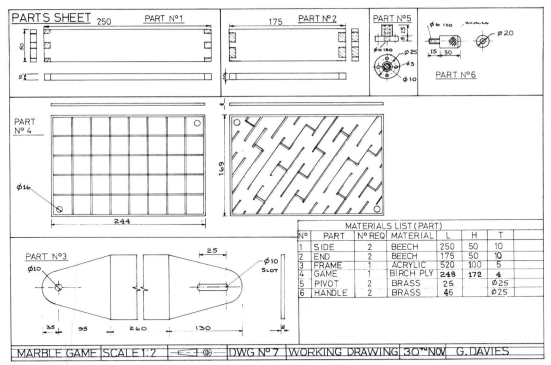

Fig. 6.8

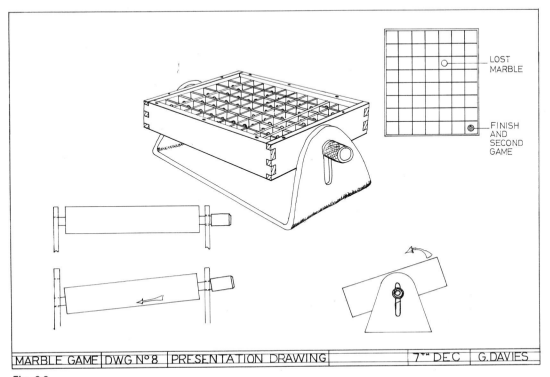

Fig. 6.9

Marble game

6.2 MOBILE TOY

Design brief

A nursery playgroup would like to have a toy that can give the children a feeling of movement. Perhaps a toy that could be propelled by pushing with one foot on the ground.

Analysis	*Possible research needed*
(a) What is a nursery playgroup?	This will need research and visits to define what and how playgroups operate.
(b) How many children attend?	This will need some research.
(c) What is the age range of the children who attend?	Important to research this point.
(d) What are the sizes of the children who attend?	Careful research to be done.
(e) Where do nursery playgroups take place?	Church halls, community centres, sports centres.
(f) What type of hall or room is used?	Research the space and size.
(g) What type of storage space is available for toys and equipment?	Check these details on visit.
(h) What other details may be required from a visit to the playgroup?	Playing surface (e.g. concrete, lino, tiles etc.)

Re-statement of design brief

Design a toy for children 3–5 years old that can be propelled by using one foot. It must be able to be used in a confined space and store easily.

Analysis of toy	*Answer*
(a) What are the possible body positions for propelling a toy forward with one foot?	Laid flat, sitting, standing, standing with support. (Experiment with a board and skate).
(b) How will body position affect the toy?	The toy shape and size will alter a great deal.
(c) In what way can the toy be moved forward?	Slide on runners or a flat surface, rollers, wheels, casters, balls.
(d) What materials would be suitable for the toy?	The materials will need to be tough and strong, yet as light as possible. It must be able to withstand misuse but be easily carried. METAL – aluminium, mild steel tube WOOD – beech, ash PLASTIC – GRP, nylon, polypropylene
(e) What construction methods should be used?	This will depend on the material, but they should be simple yet strong, with little that can be removed by small fingers.

(f) In what ways must the toy be made safe?

It must support the body and not tilt over. All edges and corners must be rounded (BS 5665 – Safety of Toys).

(g) What surface finish should the toy have?

It will need to be hard and strong; able to withstand misuse. Yet it should be colourful and attractive to small children. Suggest polyurethane paint or varnish.

(h) Does the toy need to fold away for storage?

Storage space seems to cope with a fixed toy, although one cupboard was quite small.

(i) Is there a limit to the cost?

As the fees are small and hire charges are quite high the cost should be as low as possible. £5.

(j) What time is available?

School design time will be four 35-minute periods each week over 10 weeks.

This is how one boy tackled the problem.

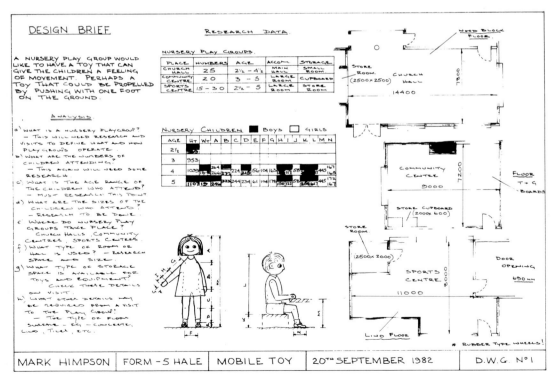

Fig. 6.10

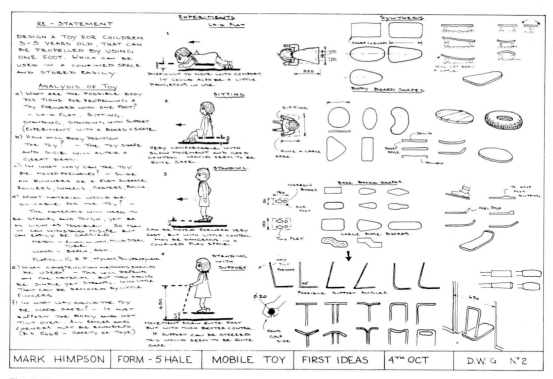

Fig. 6.11

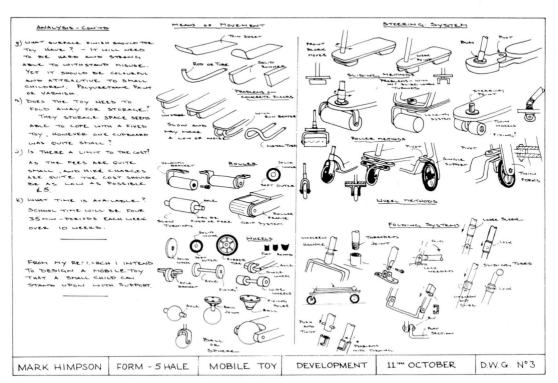

Fig. 6.12

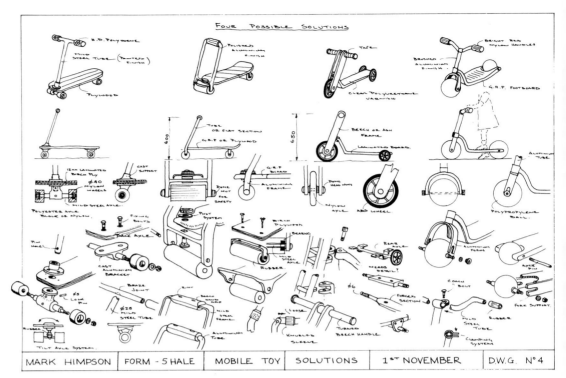

Fig. 6.13

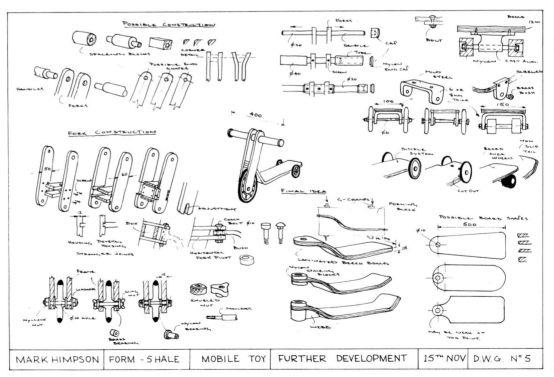

Fig. 6.14

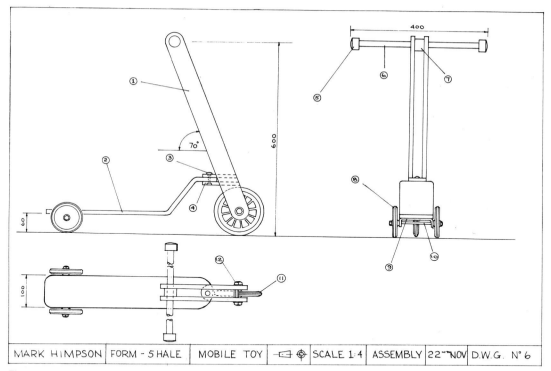

Fig. 6.15

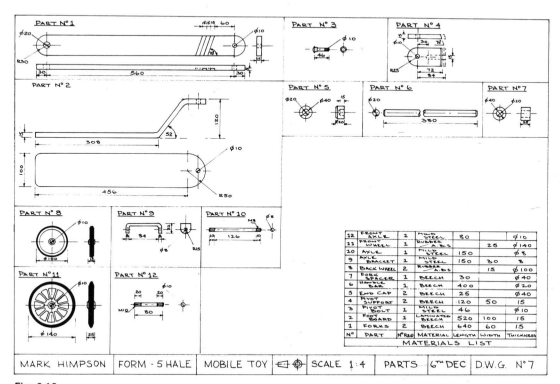

Fig. 6.16

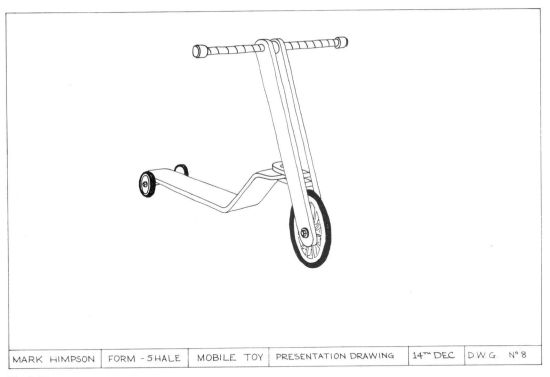

| MARK HIMPSON | FORM - SHALE | MOBILE TOY | PRESENTATION DRAWING | 14ᵀᴴ DEC | D.W.G. Nº 8 |

Fig. 6.17

6 Worked examples

Chapter 7

SAMPLE DESIGN EXAMINATION QUESTIONS

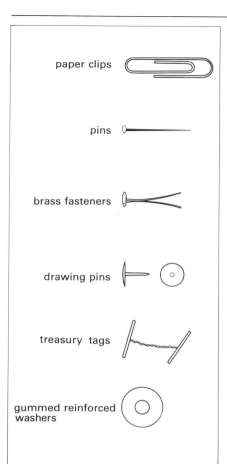

Fig. 7.1

(C – Cambridge; L – London)

1. A school has a regular supply of round section off-cuts of mild steel rod. The diameters are 3, 4, 6, 8, 10 and 12 with minimum length 30 and maximum 150. The ends have been distorted by shearing. A simple device is required to assist sorting the random lengths into lots of similar diameter.
   (a) List the design requirements that the device must fulfil.
   (b) Illustrate three different ideas that a designer could explore to reach a solution.
   (c) Identify the idea you would develop giving reasons why you think it is the best solution.
   (d) Develop this solution into a finished drawing.   (L)

2. Small quantities of stationery sundries are required to be readily available on the study of office desk. Six such items are illustrated, approximately full size, in Fig. 7.1.

   A unit has to be designed which will conveniently accommodate small quantities of these items as well as up to ten pencils or ballpoint pens. The unit can be made in any suitable material or combination of materials.

   Write a design analysis for the unit listing the problems to be solved and suggesting methods of overcoming them.   (L)

3. A design for a chess set and board is required. It is to be presented to the winning school in a chess tournament. The organising committee are seeking a non-traditional design for the chess pieces that could be made in one or more materials in keeping with the selected design.

   Prepare designs for the chess pieces and board. The chess pieces to be drawn are the King, Queen, Bishop, Knight, Rook and Pawn. The board is to be a single flat surface in two contrasting colours or textures which need not necessarily be the traditional black and white.

   Fig. 7.2 shows part of the conventional chess set showing the named pieces.   (L)

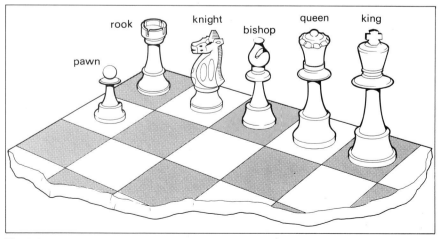

Fig. 7.2

4. A theatre company needs to be able to hold open the exit doors firmly at the end of each performance.

Design a latching device that will hold a door back against a wall. It must be able to be operated by simply pushing the door open whereupon the door will be firmly held.

The locking device must not be able to be released by the pressure of people against the door, shaking it as they push past. There should be, though, a quick and easily operated release that the user can operate when people have left to allow the door to return to the closed position.

The door is made of solid wood 35mm thick. (L)

5. A cabinet to house cassette tapes, books and magazines is required for a teenager's room. Prepare a design for a cabinet which conforms to the following specifications:

   (a) it is to be fixed to a wall and the top of the cabinet is to be below eye level;

   (b) at least 20 cassettes are to be stored. Your design should indicate the exact number for which you are catering;

   (c) provision is to be made for a small number of books and magazines of various sizes;

   (d) solid wood is to be used for the two sides of the cabinet.

The solution must conform to the sizes shown in Fig. 7.3. (L)

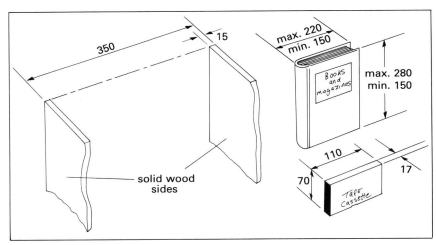

Fig. 7.3

6. A loudspeaker 340 high x 200 wide x 150 deep is to be mounted above head height onto a wall of a school's music room. Prepare a design for the mounting bracket that conforms to the following specification:

   (a) be capable of supporting a speaker cabinet of weight 2.5kg;

   (b) have an adequate wall anchorage. The speaker cabinet is made from 18 thick veneered chipboard. The back is 12 thick plywood;

   (c) be so constructed that the speaker shall have an adjustment movement from the horizontal to 15° below the horizontal and a 20° movement each side of the vertical. (L)

7. When a classical guitar player performs he or she usually sits with one foot raised on a special support. This allows for a comfortable playing position.

Prepare a design for a foot support for a guitarist that conforms to the following specifications:
(a) the support is to have two height positions of approximately 140 and 170 respectively;
(b) it should slope upwards from the back to the front i.e. from heel to toe;
(c) it should fold flat for convenience of carrying;
(d) it should be stable in use. (L)

8. Fig. 7.4 shows the overall size of a roll of perforated kitchen paper as supplied for domestic use. Prepare a design for a paper holder to the following specifications:
(a) It is to be made mainly, but not necessarily exclusively, of either solid wood or manufactured board.
(b) Paper rolls must be easily replaceable.
(c) The paper is to be protected by a cover.
(d) There must be a suitable arrangement to assist tearing of the paper.
(e) The holder is to be wall mounted.

    (i) With a long edge of your paper, placed horizontally rule a vertical line 200 from the left hand edge. To the left of this line write out a full design analysis for the holder which covers all aspects of the problems. Set out each aspect clearly and letter each for reference.
    (ii) On the right hand side of the line make preliminary sketch solutions for each of the problems stated, lettering them to conform with your solutions in answer to (i).
    (iii) Prepare a freehand sketch or sketches that clearly show the general overall outline of the final solution.
    (iv) Make a full size production drawing in orthographic projection giving all constructional details required to enable the holder to be made. Use sections, scrap views, full size orthographic details, freehand sketches etc. if further clarification is required.

Clearly letter each part of your solutions (a), (b), (c) etc., to conform with your analysis. (L)

9. The holder you have just designed in question 8 provides a solution to the problem using wood as the main material.

By means of annotated sketches show how the choice of another material would alter your design.

Select one of the following to illustrate your answer:
(a) acrylic sheet
(b) Glass Reinforced Plastic
(c) anodising quality 1.20 (18 SWG) aluminium sheet. (L)

10. The Design and Technology Department of a school has been asked to supply several desk units to be used by the school administrative staff. A unit houses two identical trays.

Prepare a design for a desk filing unit that conforms to the following specifications:
(a) the trays will be supported one above the other to economise on space;
(b) each tray is to be capable of holding 50 sheets of A4 paper (295 x 210);
(c) easy selection and removal of papers is to be ensured;
(d) both trays to be removable without disturbing the stability of the unit. (L)

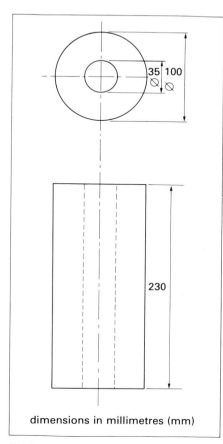

dimensions in millimetres (mm)

Fig. 7.4

11. You are to prepare a design for a money container, both coins and notes, which is to conform to the following specifications:
- (a) the container is to be used as a money box by a young child;
- (b) it is to have accommodation for at least 20 of each of the coins listed below;
- (c) coins of different denominations are to be stored separately;
- (d) there must be provision for bank notes/postal orders to be inserted and stored separately;
- (e) it must be possible to see sufficient of the coins to check the contents;
- (f) the contents are to be reasonably secure although a lock is not required;
- (g) the container is to be made mainly, but not necessarily exclusively, of plastics;
- (h) it must be possible to make the container using the facilities of a school workshop.

Details of coin and note sizes:

£1	145 x 76
50 pence	allow 32 x 2.5 thick
10 pence	$\varnothing$ 28 x 2.2 thick
5 pence	$\varnothing$ 22 x 2.2 thick
2 pence	$\varnothing$ 26 x 2 thick

Before possible sketch solutions are made several problems will have to be considered which will form part of your analysis e.g. the arrangements for the insertion and storage of coins and notes; the choice of materials available and their suitability for the stated problem; the possible utilisation of colour and combinations of colour. (You may use colour in your preparatory design work but *not* in your final working drawing).

- (a) With a long edge of your paper, AB17, placed horizontally rule a vertical line 200 from the left-hand edge. To the left of this line write out a full design analysis for the money container which covers all aspects of the problems you have to solve. Set out each aspect clearly and letter each for reference.
- (b) On the right-hand side of the line make preliminary sketch solutions for each of the problems stated, lettering them to conform with the brief given above.

Answer parts (c) *and* (d) *on a separate sheet of drawing paper.*

- (c) Sketch clearly the general outline of the final solution you have evolved.
- (d) Make detail drawings in orthographic projection of the various parts of the container and of any formers needed for its production. These drawings should show all constructional details to enable the container to be made. Your drawings may be done *either* with instruments to a full-size scale *or* freehand to approximately full size.
  (L)

Chapter 8

SAMPLE TECHNOLOGY EXAMINATION QUESTIONS

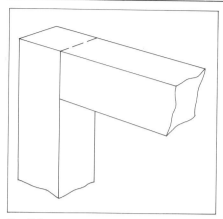

Fig. 8.1

Fig. 8.2

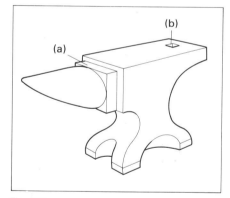

Fig. 8.3

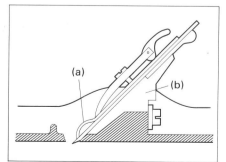

Fig. 8.4

(C – Cambridge; L – London)

1. Give one example of each of the following types of tree:
   (a) coniferous
   (b) deciduous. (C)

2. What would be a suitable finish for each of the following?
   (a) a copper dish
   (b) a mild steel television stand. (C)

3. The listed items are often made from a plastic material. Name the most suitable plastic for each of the following:
   (a) a rainwater guttering
   (b) a domestic 13-amp electric socket. (C)

4. Outline drawings for a wooden corner joint are shown. (Fig. 8.1)

   Complete the diagram to show an acceptable strong frame joint. Name the selected joint. (C)

5. A section through a wooden mould to be used in a sand casting is shown. (Fig. 8.2)
   (a) What is the name given to the slope at the sides?
   (b) Why is it necessary? (C)

6. Give an example of an item made by the blow moulding process. (C)

7. By using heat, how would you seal the end of a polythene bag? (C)

8. Name the tool you would use for marking a line parallel to the edge of a piece of:
   (a) timber
   (b) mild steel. (C)

9. What process would you perform on parts (a) and (b) of the anvil shown in Fig. 8.3? (C)

10. What is the name and function of each of the labelled parts of the steel plane shown in Fig. 8.4.
    (a) ....
    (b) ....(C)

11. What is a typical value for the included angle (shown in Fig. 8.5) for a twist drill used for drilling?
    (a) mild steel
    (b) nylon

    Give a reason for these angles being different. (C)

12. Name the material from which you would expect a surface plate to be made. Give a reason for this choice of material. (C)

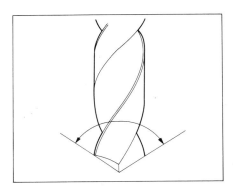

Fig. 8.5

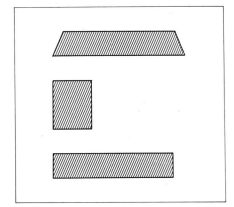

Fig. 8.6

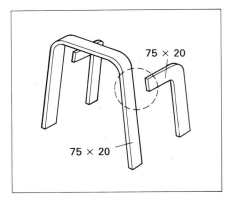

Fig. 8.7

13. Three different types of wood chisel blade are shown in cross section. Name each. (Fig. 8.6)
(a) ....
(b) ....
(c) ....
For any two of these, give examples of their uses. (C)

14. In what three basic material forms are plastics obtainable for use in the workshop?
(a) ....
(b) ....
(c) ....(C)

15. Show a cross section of a hot line bender, as used when heating plastic prior to bending. (C)

16. What hand tools would you expect to use in the following processes?
(a) Cutting along the length of a deal plank 25mm thick.
(b) Making a triangular hole through a piece of 6mm plywood. (C)

17. Draw the BS symbol for 1st and 3rd angle projection and state which projection it represents. (C)

18. What special personal protection should be used when carrying out the following processes?
(a) wood turning
(b) injection moulding
(c) forgework (C)

19. Can you suggest two methods of joining the pieces shown, when they are made from:
(a) wood
(b) metal
(c) plastic?
Explain one method in detail, how the work is prepared, joining and the tools and equipment used. (C)

20. By effecting certain changes, the initial strength of some materials can be improved. Amongst the possible changes are:
(a) a modification of the material itself;
(b) an alteration of an established form of construction;
(c) an alteration of the basic form in which the materials are manufactured.

(i) State one specific method of strengthening each of the following materials: wood, metal and plastics.
(ii) For *two* of the three examples describe in detail the process whereby strengthening is achieved. (L)

21. A pattern used in sand casting has proved to be badly designed. Explain how it could be improved, what material it should be made from, and how it would be moulded in the sand. (Fig. 8.8) (C)

22. (a) Screws are frequently used to join materials. State one advantage and one disadvantage of using metal woodscrews for wood to wood joints, and metal machine screws for metal to metal joints.

8 Sample technology examination questions

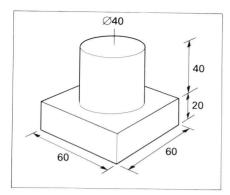

Fig. 8.8

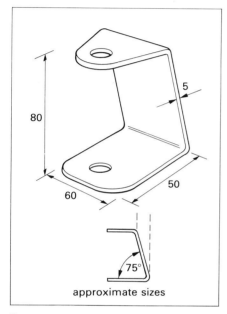

approximate sizes

Fig. 8.9

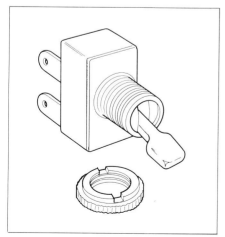

Fig. 8.10

(b) Sketch two different screw head shapes and two different screw head styles to accept screwdrivers.

(c) State two advantages of using self-tapping screws in sheet metal or plastics.

(d) By means of a sectional view show how the appropriate screw holds together either two pieces of wood or two pieces of metal.   (C)

23. The following shape in a thin material is to be made as a simple pen holder. (Fig. 8.9).

How could the shape be made in two of the following materials?
(a) brass
(b) acrylic
(c) mahogany

State in each case the correct method to use, mentioning in particular any special tools or formers that are appropriate.   (C)

24. Some electrical components are attached to the panel by means of a slotted threaded ring, as shown in Fig. 8.10.

DATA:

Switch/spindle protrudes	30
Thread diameter	10
Ring diameter	18
thickness	5
Slots – width	1.3
depth	1.5
Bevel	0.5 × 45°

Design a tool to tighten the ring to the following specification. It must
(a) fit the slots either side of the threaded hole of ⌀ 10,
(b) allow a 30 long switch lever or spindle to protrude through the hole,
(c) be of a material and in a condition to enable it to be used without wearing.

Present your answer in the form of a large annotated sketch. Give full details for its manufacture, including materials, construction, functional dimensions and finish. Credit will be given for simplicity of design, ease of manufacture, ease of operation and the economic use of materials.   (L)

25. You are asked to make a condiment set for salt, pepper and mustard.
(a) Show a suitable design paying particular attention to your choice of materials. Say why you have made your choice.
(b) Describe fully all joining processes needed.   (C)

26. Discuss the advantages and disadvantages of steel, aluminium and GRP in the manufacture of car bodies and other similar applications.   (C)

27. Which material do you associate with the following processes? Describe each process and its effect on the selected material.
(a) annealing
(b) case hardening
(c) shaping with a hot wire cutter
(d) steam bending   (C)

Sample technology examination questions

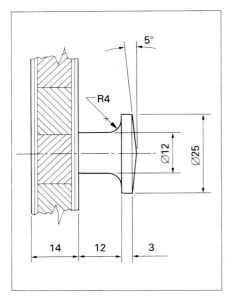

Fig. 8.11

28. Fig. 8.11 gives details of a knob, six of which are to be made for utile veneered cupboard doors. The method of fixing the knobs to the doors is not shown. The turned knobs could be made from either ebony or duralumin or black nylon.

(a) Select one of the above materials and make a clear sketch of how the knob would be fixed to the door.

(b) Use the headings below to decribe how you would turn the knob.

Process No.	Process	Sketches	Tools
1			
2			(L)

29. *Either* Name the ferrous alloys used for making the following parts of an engineer's vice:

(a) jaw plates

(b) body

(c) screw and tommy bar.

Describe the production of *one* of these alloys from pig iron.

A garden bench is to be made of teak, an easy chair of oak and a kitchen stool of pine. Briefly list the major characteristics of each of these materials and state why each is particularly suited to its intended use.

Describe the final stages of cleaning up, preparation for and application of a suitable protective finish to *one* of these seats. (L)

8 Sample technology examination questions

INDEX